AS-Level
Biology

LRC Stoke Park
GUILDFORD COLLEGE

AS Biology is seriously tricky — no question about that.
To do well, you're going to need to revise properly and practise hard.

This book has thorough notes on all the theory you need,
and it's got practice questions... lots of them.
For every topic there are warm-up and exam-style questions.

And of course, we've done our best to make the whole thing vaguely entertaining for you.

Complete Revision and Practice
Exam Board: Edexcel

Published by CGP

Editors:
Amy Boutal, Ellen Bowness, Joe Brazier, Charlotte Burrows, Tom Cain, Katherine Craig,
Andy Park, Laurence Stamford, Jane Towle.

Contributors:
Gloria Barnett, Jessica Egan, Liz Masters, Adrian Schmit, Sophie Watkins, Anna-fe Williamson.

Proofreaders:
Sue Hocking, Glenn Rogers.

ISBN: 978 1 84762 120 7

With thanks to Jan Greenway for the copyright research.

Data used to construct the graph on page 21 from P.M. Ridker, et al. Comparison of C-reactive protein and low-density lipoprotein cholesterol levels in the prediction of first cardiovascular events. NEJM 2002; 347: 1557-65.

Data used to construct the top graph on page 24 reproduced with kind permission from Oxford University Press. P. Reynolds, et al. Active Smoking, Household Passive Smoking, and Breast Cancer: Evidence From the California Teachers Study. JNCI 2004; 96(1):29-37

Data used to construct the bottom graph on page 24 from Hamajima, N. Hirose, K. Tajima, K. et al. Alcohol, tobacco and breast cancer - collaborative reanalysis of individual data from 53 epidemiological studies, including 58,515 women with breast cancer and 95,067 women without the disease. BJC 2002; 87:1234-45

Data used to construct the graph on page 25 from R. Doll, R. Peto, J. Boreham, I Sutherland. Mortality in relation to smoking: 50 years' observations on male British doctors. BMJ 2004; 328:1519.

With thanks to Science Photo Library for permission to reproduce the photographs used on pages 49 and 65.

Graph of breast cancer and family history on page 59 reprinted from the Lancet, Vol number 358, Familial breast cancer: collaborative reanalysis of individual data from 52 epidemiological studies including 58209 women with breast cancer and 101986 women without the disease, 1389 -1399, Copyright 2001, With permission from Elsevier.

Graph of breast cancer and alcohol consumption on page 59 from Hamajima, N. Hirose, K. Tajima, K. et al. Alcohol, tobacco and breast cancer - collaborative reanalysis of individual data from 53 epidemiological studies, including 58,515 women with breast cancer and 95,067 women without the disease. BJC 2002; 87:1234-45

Groovy website: www.cgpbooks.co.uk
Jolly bits of clipart from CorelDRAW®
Printed by Elanders Ltd, Newcastle upon Tyne.

Based on the classic CGP style created by Richard Parsons.

WITHDRAWN # Contents

The Scientific Process

'How Science Works' is all about the scientific process — how we develop and test scientific ideas.
It's what scientists do all day, every day (well, except at coffee time — never come between a scientist and their coffee).

Scientists Come Up with **Theories** — Then **Test Them**...

Science tries to explain **how** and **why** things happen — it **answers questions**. It's all about seeking and gaining **knowledge** about the world around us. Scientists do this by **asking** questions and **suggesting** answers and then **testing** them, to see if they're correct — this is the **scientific process**.

1) **Ask** a question — make an **observation** and ask **why or how** it happens.
   E.g. why is trypsin (an enzyme) found in the small intestine but not in the stomach?

2) **Suggest** an answer, or part of an answer, by forming a **theory** (a possible **explanation** of the observations) e.g. pH affects the activity of enzymes. (Scientists also sometimes form a **model** too — a **simplified picture** of what's physically going on.)

3) Make a **prediction** or **hypothesis** — a **specific testable statement**, based on the theory, about what will happen in a test situation. E.g. trypsin will be active at pH 8 (the pH of the small intestine) but inactive at pH 2 (the pH of the stomach).

4) Carry out a **test** — to provide **evidence** that will support the prediction (or help to disprove it). E.g. measure the rate of reaction of trypsin at various pH levels.

The evidence supported Quentin's Theory of Flammable Burps.

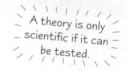

A theory is only scientific if it can be tested.

...Then They **Tell** Everyone About Their **Results**...

The results are **published** — scientists need to let others know about their work. Scientists publish their results in **scientific journals**. These are just like normal magazines, only they contain **scientific reports** (called papers) instead of the latest celebrity gossip.

1) Scientific reports are similar to the **lab write-ups** you do in school. And just as a lab write-up is **reviewed** (marked) by your teacher, reports in scientific journals undergo **peer review** before they're published.

2) The report is sent out to **peers** — other scientists who are experts in the **same area**. They examine the data and results, and if they think that the conclusion is reasonable it's **published**. This makes sure that work published in scientific journals is of a **good standard**.

3) But peer review **can't guarantee** the science is **correct** — other scientists still need to **reproduce** it.

4) Sometimes **mistakes** are made and flawed work is published. Peer review **isn't perfect** but it's probably the best way for scientists to self-regulate their work and to publish **quality reports**.

...Then **Other Scientists** Will **Test** the Theory Too

Other scientists read the published theories and results, and try to **test the theory** themselves. This involves:

• Repeating the **exact same experiments**.
• Using the theory to make **new predictions** and then testing them with **new experiments**.

If the **Evidence** Supports a Theory, It's **Accepted** — for Now

1) If all the experiments in all the world provide good evidence to back it up, the theory is thought of as **scientific 'fact'** (for now).

2) But it will never become **totally indisputable** fact. Scientific **breakthroughs or advances** could provide new ways to question and test the theory, which could lead to **new evidence** that **conflicts** with the current evidence. Then the testing starts all over again...

And this, my friend, is the **tentative nature of scientific knowledge** — it's always **changing** and **evolving**.

The Scientific Process

So scientists need evidence to back up their theories. They get it by carrying out experiments, and when that's not possible they carry out studies. But why bother with science at all? We want to know as much as possible so we can use it to try and improve our lives (and because we're nosy).

Evidence Comes from Lab Experiments...

1) Results from **controlled experiments** in **laboratories** are **great**.
2) A lab is the easiest place to **control variables** so that they're all **kept constant** (except for the one you're investigating).
3) This means you can draw meaningful **conclusions**.

> For example, if you're investigating how temperature affects the rate of an enzyme-controlled reaction you need to keep everything but the temperature constant, e.g. the pH of the solution, the concentration of the solution etc.

...and Well-Designed Studies

1) There are things you **can't** investigate in a lab, e.g. whether stress causes heart attacks. You have to do a study instead.
2) You still need to try and make the study as controlled as possible to make it **more reliable**. But in reality it's **very hard** to control **all the variables** that **might** be having an effect.
3) You can do things to help, e.g. have **matched groups** — **choose two groups** of people (those who have quite stressful jobs and those who don't) who are **as similar as possible** (same mix of ages, same mix of diets etc.). But you can't easily rule out every possibility.

Samantha thought her study was very well designed — especially the fitted bookshelf.

See pages 76-78 for more on study design.

Society Makes Decisions Based on Scientific Evidence

1) Lots of scientific work eventually leads to **important discoveries** or breakthroughs that could **benefit humankind**.
2) These results are **used by society** (that's you, me and everyone else) to **make decisions** — about the way we live, what we eat, what we drive, etc.
3) All sections of society use scientific evidence to make decisions, e.g. politicians use it to devise policies and individuals use science to make decisions about their own lives.

Other factors can **influence** decisions about science or the way science is used:

Economic factors

- Society has to consider the **cost** of implementing changes based on scientific conclusions — e.g. the **NHS** can't afford the most expensive drugs without **sacrificing** something else.
- Scientific research is **expensive** so companies won't always develop new ideas — e.g. developing new drugs is costly, so pharmaceutical companies often only invest in drugs that are likely to make them **money**.

Social factors

- **Decisions** affect **people's lives** — E.g. scientists may suggest **banning smoking** and **alcohol** to prevent health problems, but shouldn't **we** be able to **choose** whether **we** want to smoke and drink or not?

Environmental factors

- Scientists believe **unexplored regions** like remote parts of rainforests might contain **untapped drug** resources. But some people think we shouldn't **exploit** these regions because any interesting finds may lead to **deforestation** and **reduced biodiversity** in these areas.

So there you have it — how science works...

Hopefully these pages have given you a nice intro to how science works, e.g. what scientists do to provide you with 'facts'. You need to understand this, as you're expected to know how science works — for the exam and for life.

Water

Your body needs all sorts of different molecules to stay alive, and this section covers all the major groups.
I know water's not the most stimulating topic to start the book with, but life can't exist without water
— in fact, everyday water is one of the most important substances on the planet. Funny old world.

Water is Vital to Living Organisms

Water makes up about 80% of a cell's contents. It has some important
functions, inside and outside cells:

1)   Water is a **solvent**, which means some substances **dissolve**
in it. Most biological reactions take place **in solution**,
so water's pretty essential.

2)   Water **transports** substances. Substances can be transported **more
easily** if they're **dissolved** in a solvent. So the fact that water's a
liquid and a **solvent** means it can easily transport all sorts of
materials, like glucose and oxygen, around plants and animals.

*As her face slowly dissolved,
Jenny cursed her holiday.*

Water Molecules have a Simple Structure

Examiners like asking you to relate **structure** to **properties** and **function**,
so make sure you're clear on the structure of water.

1)   A molecule of **water (H_2O)** is **one atom** of **oxygen (O)**
joined to **two atoms** of **hydrogen (H_2)** by **shared electrons**.

2)   Because the **shared negative**
hydrogen electrons are
pulled towards the oxygen
atom, the other side of each
hydrogen atom is left with a
slight positive charge.

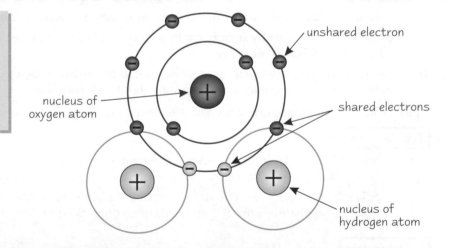

unshared electron

nucleus of
oxygen atom

shared electrons

nucleus of
hydrogen atom

3)   The **unshared** negative
electrons on the oxygen
atom give it a **slight
negative charge**.

4)   This makes water a **dipolar** molecule
— it has a negative charge on one side
and a positive charge on the other.

negatively
charged side

positively
charged side

5)   The **negatively charged oxygen atoms** of water **attract** the
positively charged hydrogen atoms of other water molecules.

6)   This attraction is called
hydrogen bonding.

Water

Water's **Structure** is Related to its **Functions**

The **structure of a water molecule** gives it some useful **properties**, and these help to explain many of its **functions**:

Water's **Dipole Nature** Makes it **Very Cohesive**

1) Cohesion is the **attraction** between molecules of the same type (e.g. two water molecules). Water molecules are **very cohesive** (they tend to stick together) because they're **dipolar**.

2) This helps water to **flow**, making it great for **transporting substances**.

Water's **Dipole Nature** Also Makes it a **Good Solvent**

1) A lot of important substances in biological reactions are **ionic** (like **salt**, for example). This means they're made from **one positively charged** atom or molecule and **one negatively charged** atom or molecule (e.g. salt is made from a positive sodium ion and a negative chloride ion).

2) Because water is dipolar, the **positive end** of a water molecule will be attracted to the **negative ion**, and the **negative end** of a water molecule will be attracted to the **positive ion**.

3) This means the ions will get **totally surrounded** by water molecules — in other words, they'll **dissolve**.

4) So water's **dipole nature** makes it useful as a **solvent** for other polar molecules.

> Remember — a molecule is _dipolar_ if it has a negatively charged bit and a positively charged bit.

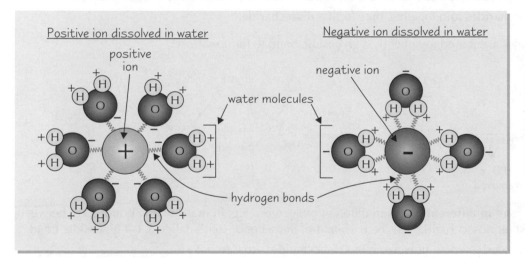

The dipolar nature of bears sometimes results in unexpected attraction.

Practice Questions

Q1 Briefly describe what is meant by a dipolar molecule.

Q2 What is cohesion?

Exam Questions

Q1 Describe, with the aid of a diagram, the structure of a water molecule. [3 marks]

Q2 Relate the structure of water to its ability to transport substances. [6 marks]

Pssssssssssssssssssssssssssssssssssssssssssssss — need the loo yet?

Water is pretty darn useful really. It looks so, well, dull — but in fact it's scientifically amazing, and essential for all kinds of jobs — like transporting things around the body. You need to learn its structure so that you can relate its solvent properties to its function as a transport molecule. Right, I'm off — when you gotta go, you gotta go.

Carbohydrates

Carbohydrates are dead important chemicals — for a start they're the main energy supply in living organisms. Unfortunately they look a bit boring, but don't let that put you off...

Carbohydrates are Made from Monosaccharides

1) Most carbohydrates are **large**, complex molecules composed of **long chains** of **monosaccharides** (e.g. starch is a large carbohydrate composed of long chains of glucose)

2) **Single** monosaccharides are also called carbohydrates though.

3) **Glucose** is a monosaccharide with **six carbon** atoms in each molecule.

4) There are **two types** of glucose — **alpha (α)** and **beta (β)** — but you only need to learn about alpha-glucose for this section.

5) Glucose's **structure** is related to its **function** as the main **energy source** in animals and plants. Its structure makes it **soluble** so it can be **easily transported**, and its chemical bonds contain **lots of energy**.

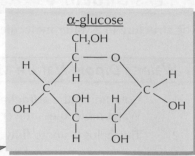

α-glucose

Monosaccharides Join Together to Form Disaccharides and Polysaccharides

1) Monosaccharides are **joined together** by **glycosidic bonds** in a **condensation reaction** (a reaction where a molecule of **water** is **released**).

2) A **hydrogen** atom on one monosaccharide bonds to a **hydroxyl** (OH) group on the other, releasing a molecule of water.

3) The **reverse** of this is a **hydrolysis reaction** — a molecule of water reacts with the glycosidic bond, **breaking it apart**.

4) When **two monosaccharides** join together, they form a **disaccharide**:

Two α–glucose molecules are joined together by a **glycosidic bond** to form **maltose**:

CH₂OH ... glucose + glucose → (condensation / hydrolysis) → maltose + H₂O. H₂O is removed. glycosidic bond.

Glycosidic bonds can form in **different places** in different molecules. E.g. in **maltose**, the bonds form between the **carbon 1** of the first monosaccharide and the **carbon 4** of the second, so it's called a **1-4 glycosidic bond**.

As well as maltose, you need to know how two other disaccharides are formed:

- **Lactose** — **β–glucose** and **galactose** with a **1-4** glycosidic bond.
- **Sucrose** — **α–glucose** and **fructose** with a **1-2** glycosidic bond.

1-4 glycosidic bond

5) A **polysaccharide** is formed when **more than two monosaccharides** join together:

Lots of α–glucose molecules are joined together by **1-4 glycosidic bonds** to form **amylose**:

glycosidic bonds. CH₂OH ... glucose ... glucose ... glucose ... glucose ... glucose

As well as amylose, you need to know how two other polysaccharides are formed:

- **Amylopectin** — **α–glucose** with **1-4 and 1-6** glycosidic bonds, with lots of **side branches** (see next page).
- **Glycogen** — **α–glucose** with **1-4 and 1-6** glycosidic bonds and **even more** side branches than amylopectin.

Carbohydrates

You Need to Learn About **Two Polysaccharides**

You need to know about the relationship between the **structure** and **function** of two polysaccharides:

1) **Starch** — the main **energy storage material** in **plants**

1) Cells get **energy** from **glucose**. Plants **store** excess glucose as **starch** (when a plant **needs more glucose** for energy it **breaks down** starch to release the glucose).

2) Starch is a mixture of **two** polysaccharides of **alpha-glucose** — amylose and **amylopectin**:

- **Amylose** — a long, **unbranched chain** of glucose joined together with **1-4 glycosidic bonds**. The angles of the glycosidic bonds give it a **coiled structure**, almost like a cylinder. This makes it **compact**, so it's really **good for storage** because you can **fit more in** to a small space.

- **Amylopectin** — a long, **branched chain** of glucose that contains **1-4 and 1-6 glycosidic bonds**. Its **side branches** allow the **enzymes** that break down the molecule to get at the **glycosidic bonds easily**. This means that the glucose can be **released quickly**.

3) Starch is also **insoluble** in water, so it **doesn't** cause water to enter cells by **osmosis** (which would make them swell). This makes it good for **storage**.

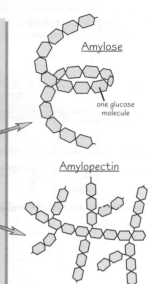
Amylose
one glucose molecule

Amylopectin

2) **Glycogen** — the main **energy storage material** in **animals**

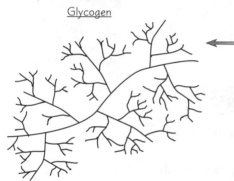
Glycogen

1) Animal cells get **energy** from **glucose** too. But animals **store** excess glucose as **glycogen** — another polysaccharide of **alpha-glucose**.

2) Its structure is very similar to amylopectin (it has **1-4 and 1-6 glycosidic bonds**), except that it has **loads** more **side branches** coming off it. Loads of branches means that stored glucose can be **released quickly**, which is **important for energy release** in animals.

3) It's also a very **compact** molecule, so it's good for storage.

4) Like starch, glycogen's also **insoluble** in water, so it doesn't cause cells to swell by osmosis.

5) It's a **large molecule**, so it can store **lots of energy**.

Practice Questions

Q1 What type of bonds hold monosaccharide molecules together in a polysaccharide?

Q2 Name the two monosaccharides that join together to form lactose.

Q3 Name the two different types of polysaccharide that form starch.

Q4 What is the function of glycogen?

Exam Questions

Q1 Describe, with the aid of a diagram, how glycosidic bonds are formed and broken in living organisms. [8 marks]

Q2 Describe the structure of starch and relate it to its function. [10 marks]

Mmmmm, starch... Tasty, tasty chips and beans... *dribble*. Ahem, sorry.

Remember that condensation and hydrolysis reactions are the reverse of each other. You need to learn how disaccharides and polysaccharides are formed and broken down by these reactions. And don't forget that starch is composed of two different polysaccharides... and that one of them is really similar to glycogen... so many reminders, so little space...

Lipids

Right, that's water and carbohydrates dealt with. But there's another important kind of molecule you need to know about, and that's lipids, or 'fatty oily things' to you and me.

Triglycerides are a Kind of Lipid

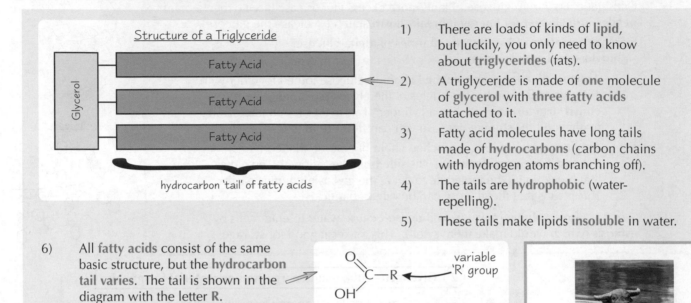

Structure of a Triglyceride

hydrocarbon 'tail' of fatty acids

1) There are loads of kinds of **lipid**, but luckily, you only need to know about **triglycerides** (fats).

2) A triglyceride is made of **one** molecule of **glycerol** with **three fatty acids** attached to it.

3) Fatty acid molecules have long tails made of **hydrocarbons** (carbon chains with hydrogen atoms branching off).

4) The tails are **hydrophobic** (water-repelling).

5) These tails make lipids **insoluble** in water.

6) All **fatty acids** consist of the same basic structure, but the **hydrocarbon tail varies**. The tail is shown in the diagram with the letter **R**.

variable 'R' group

Contrary to popular belief, cows aren't hydrophobic.

Triglycerides are Formed by Condensation Reactions

1) Like carbohydrates, triglycerides are formed by **condensation reactions** and broken up by **hydrolysis reactions**.

2) Three **fatty acids** and a single **glycerol molecule** are joined together by **ester bonds**.

3) A **hydrogen** atom on the glycerol molecule bonds to a **hydroxyl** (OH) group on the fatty acid, **releasing** a molecule of **water**.

4) The **reverse** happens in **hydrolysis** — a molecule of water is added to **each ester bond** to break it apart, and the triglyceride **splits up** into three fatty acids and one glycerol molecule.

Each of the fatty acids in a triglyceride is attached to the glycerol molecule by an ester bond.

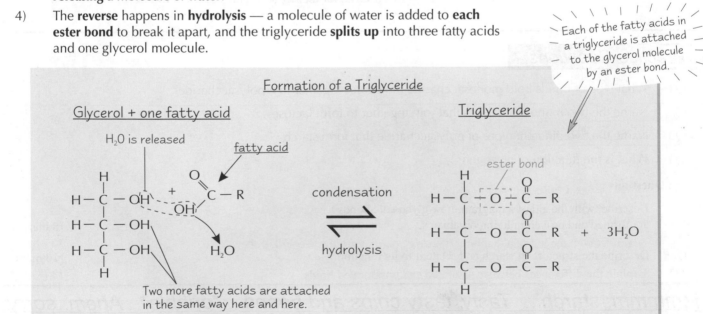

Formation of a Triglyceride

Glycerol + one fatty acid

Triglyceride

H₂O is released

fatty acid

condensation

hydrolysis

ester bond

Two more fatty acids are attached in the same way here and here.

Lipids

Lipids can be **Saturated** or **Unsaturated**

1) There are two types of lipids — **saturated** lipids and **unsaturated** lipids.

2) **Saturated** lipids are mainly found in **animal fats** (e.g. butter) and **unsaturated** lipids are mostly found in **plants** (e.g. olive oil).

3) Unsaturated lipids **melt at lower temperatures** than saturated ones.
   That's why margarine's easier to spread than butter straight out of the fridge.

4) The difference between these two types of lipids is their **hydrocarbon tails**.

Saturated

Saturated lipids **don't** have any **double bonds** between the **carbon atoms** in their hydrocarbon tails — every carbon is attached to at least two **hydrogen** atoms. The lipid is 'saturated' with hydrogen.

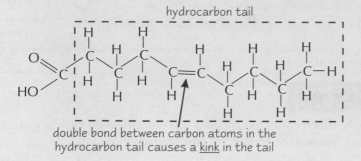

Unsaturated

Unsaturated lipids **do** have **double bonds** between the **carbon atoms** in their hydrocarbon tails. These double bonds cause the chain to kink. If they have **two or more** of them, the lipid is called **polyunsaturated**.

double bond between carbon atoms in the hydrocarbon tail causes a <u>kink</u> in the tail

Sure, unsaturated lipids are kinky, but not as kinky as Bernard.

Practice Questions

Q1 Briefly describe the structure of a triglyceride.

Q2 What type of bonds join fatty acids to glycerol in a triglyceride?

Exam Questions

Q1 Describe, with the aid of a diagram, how triglycerides are formed and broken down. [9 marks]

Q2 Explain the differences between saturated and unsaturated lipids. [4 marks]

Hydrocarbon tails, unsaturated lipids... Whatever happened to plain old lard?

You don't get far in life without extensive lard knowledge, so learn all the details on this page good and proper. Lipids pop up in other sections, so make sure you know the basics. Right, all this lipids talk is making me hungry — chips time...

Proteins

There are millions of different proteins in the body. They're the most abundant molecules in cells, making up 50% or more of a cell's dry mass — now that's just plain greedy.

Proteins are Made from Long Chains of Amino Acids

1) Proteins are made up of **lots** of **smaller molecules** (**monomers**) linked together. The monomers of proteins are **amino acids**.
2) A **dipeptide** is formed when **two** amino acids join together.
3) A **polypeptide** is formed when **more than two** amino acids join together.
4) **Proteins are made up of one or more polypeptides.**

Grant's cries of "die peptide, die" could be heard for miles around. He'd never forgiven it for sleeping with his wife.

Different Amino Acids Have Different Variable Groups

All amino acids have the same general structure — a **carboxyl group** (-COOH) and an **amino group** (-NH₂) attached to a **carbon** atom. The **difference** between different amino acids is the **variable** group (**R** on diagram) they contain.

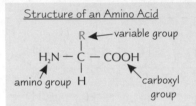

Structure of an Amino Acid

$$H_2N - \underset{\underset{H}{|}}{\overset{\overset{R}{|}}{C}} - COOH$$

variable group
amino group
carboxyl group

E.g. Structure of Glycine

$$H_2N - \underset{\underset{H}{|}}{\overset{\overset{H}{|}}{C}} - COOH$$

Glycine is the smallest amino acid — the R group is a hydrogen atom.

Amino Acids are Joined Together by Peptide Bonds

1) Amino acids are linked together by **peptide bonds** to form dipeptides and polypeptides.
2) Like carbohydrates and triglycerides, dipeptides and polypeptides are formed by **condensation reactions**.

The reverse of this reaction is a hydrolysis reaction.

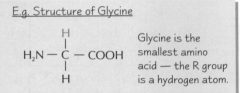

amino acid 1   amino acid 2   dipeptide

condensation

a molecule of water is formed during condensation.

peptide bond

Proteins Have Four Structural Levels

Proteins are **big**, **complicated** molecules. They're much easier to explain if you describe their structure in four 'levels'. These levels are a protein's **primary**, **secondary**, **tertiary** and **quaternary** structures.

Primary Structure — this is the **sequence** of **amino acids** in the **polypeptide chain**.

Secondary Structure — the polypeptide chain doesn't remain flat and straight. **Hydrogen bonds** form between the amino acids in the chain. This makes it automatically **coil** into an **alpha** (*α*) **helix** or **fold** into a **beta** (*β*) **pleated sheet** — this is the secondary structure.

Tertiary Structure — the coiled or folded chain of amino acids is often **coiled** and **folded further**. **More bonds** form between different parts of the polypeptide chain. For proteins made from a **single** polypeptide chain, the tertiary structure forms their **final 3D structure**.

Quaternary Structure — some proteins are made of **several different polypeptide chains** held together by **bonds**. The **quaternary structure** is the way these polypeptide chains are assembled together. For proteins made from **more than one** polypeptide chain, the quaternary structure is the protein's **final 3D structure**.

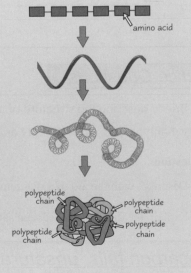

amino acid

polypeptide chain
polypeptide chain
polypeptide chain
polypeptide chain

Proteins

Different Bonds Hold Different Structural Levels Together

The four structural levels of a protein are held together by **different kinds** of **bonds**:

1) **Primary structure** — held together by the **peptide bonds** between amino acids.

2) **Secondary structure** — held together by **hydrogen bonds** that form between nearby amino acids. These bonds create **α-helix chains** or **β-pleated sheets**.

> Hydrogen bonds are weak bonds between a positive hydrogen atom in one molecule and a negative atom or group in another molecule (see p. 4).

3) **Tertiary structure** — this is affected by a few different kinds of bonds:

- **Ionic interactions**. These are **weak attractions** between **negative** and **positive** charges on different parts of the molecule.
- **Disulfide bonds**. Whenever two molecules of the amino acid **cysteine** come close together, the **sulfur atom** in one cysteine bonds to the sulfur in the other cysteine, forming a disulfide bond.
- **Hydrophobic** and **hydrophilic interactions**. When **hydrophobic** (water-repelling) groups are close together in the protein, they tend to **clump together**. This means that **hydrophilic** (water-attracting) groups are more likely to be pushed to the **outside**, which affects how the protein **folds up** into its final structure.
- **Hydrogen bonds**.

4) **Quaternary structure** — this tends to be determined by the **tertiary structure** of the individual polypeptide chains being bonded together. Because of this, it can be influenced by **all the bonds** mentioned above.

A Protein's Primary Structure Determines its 3D Structure and Properties

1) The **amino acid sequence** of a protein determines what **bonds** will form and how the protein will **fold up** into its 3D structure. E.g. if there are many cysteines, these will form **disulfide bonds** with each other, so the protein folds up in a certain way.

2) In turn, the **3D structure** of a protein determines its **properties**.

Protein 3D Structures include Globular and Fibrous

GLOBULAR

1) Globular proteins are **round**, **compact** proteins made up of **multiple polypeptide chains**.

2) The chains are **coiled up** so that **hydrophilic** (water-attracting) parts of chains are on the **outside** of the molecule and **hydrophobic** (water-repelling) parts of chains face **inwards**.

3) This makes the proteins **soluble**, so they're **easily transported** in fluids.

4) E.g. **haemoglobin** is a globular protein made of **four** polypeptide chains. It **carries oxygen** around the body in the blood. It's **soluble**, so it can be easily transported in the blood. It also has iron-containing **haem groups** that **bind** to oxygen.

haem group

polypeptide chain

FIBROUS

1) Fibrous proteins are made up of **long, insoluble polypeptide chains** that are **tightly coiled** round each other to form a **rope shape**.

2) The chains are held together by **lots of bonds** (e.g. disulfide and hydrogen bonds), which make the proteins **strong**.

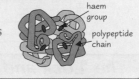

3) Because they're strong, fibrous proteins are often found in **supportive tissue**.

4) E.g. **collagen** is a **strong**, **fibrous protein** that forms supportive tissue in **animals**.

Practice Questions

Q1 Draw the basic structure of an amino acid.

Q2 Name four types of bond that determine the 3D structure of a protein.

Exam Question

Q1 Describe how a dipeptide is formed. [5 marks]

The name's Bond — Peptide Bond...

Protein structure is hard to imagine. I think of a Slinky — the wire's the primary structure, it coils up to form the secondary structure and if you coil the Slinky round your arm that's the tertiary structure. When a few Slinkys get tangled up that's like the quaternary structure. Oh, I need to get out more. I wish I had more friends and not just this stupid Slinky for company.

Enzymes

*Enzymes crop up loads in biology — they're really useful 'cos they make reactions work more quickly. So, whether you feel the need for some speed or not, read on — because you **really** need to know this basic stuff about enzymes.*

Enzymes are Biological Catalysts

Enzymes **speed up chemical reactions** by acting as **biological catalysts**.

A catalyst is a substance that speeds up a chemical reaction without being used up in the reaction itself.

1) They catalyse metabolic reactions in your body, e.g. digestion and respiration.

2) Enzyme action can be intracellular — within cells, or extracellular — outside cells (e.g. in places like the blood and digestive system).

3) Enzymes are globular proteins.

4) Enzymes have an active site, which has a specific shape. The active site is the part of the enzyme where the substrate molecules (the substance that the enzyme interacts with) bind to.

5) Enzymes are highly specific due to their 3D structure (see next page).

Enzymes Lower the Activation Energy of a Reaction

In a chemical reaction, a certain amount of **energy** needs to be supplied to the chemicals before the reaction will **start**. This is called the **activation energy** — it's often provided as **heat**. Enzymes **lower** the amount of activation energy that's needed, often making reactions happen at a **lower temperature** than they could without an enzyme. This **speeds up** the **rate of reaction**.

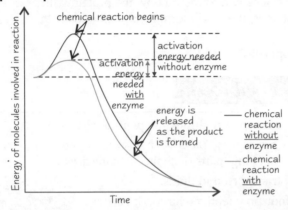

When a substrate fits into the enzyme's active site it forms an **enzyme-substrate complex** — it's this that lowers the activation energy. Here are two reasons why:

1) If two substrate molecules need to be **joined**, being attached to the enzyme holds them **close together**, **reducing** any **repulsion** between the molecules so they can bond more easily.

2) If the enzyme is catalysing a **breakdown reaction**, fitting into the active site puts a **strain** on bonds in the substrate, so the substrate molecule **breaks up** more easily.

The 'Lock and Key' Model is a Good Start...

Enzymes are a bit picky — they only work with substrates that fit their active site. Early scientists studying the action of enzymes came up with the '**lock and key**' model. This is where the **substrate fits** into the **enzyme** in the same way that a **key fits** into a **lock**. But, scientists soon realised that the lock and key model didn't give the full story. The enzyme and substrate do have to fit together in the first place, but new evidence showed that the **enzyme-substrate complex changed shape** slightly to complete the fit. This **locks** the substrate even more tightly to the enzyme. Scientists modified the old lock and key model and came up with the '**induced fit**' model.

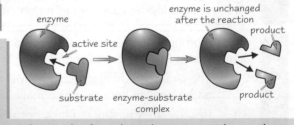

...but the 'Induced Fit' Model is a Better Theory

The '**induced fit**' model helps to explain why enzymes are so **specific** and only bond to one particular substrate. The substrate doesn't only have to be the right shape to fit the active site, it has to make the active site **change shape** in the right way as well. This is a prime example of how a widely accepted theory can **change** when **new evidence** comes along. The 'induced fit' model is still widely accepted — for now, anyway.

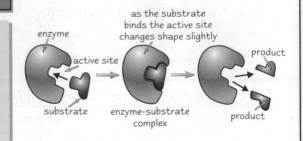

Enzymes

Enzymes are **Specific** Because of Their **3D Structure**

1) Enzymes are **very specific** — they usually only catalyse **one** reaction, e.g. maltase only breaks down maltose, sucrase only breaks down sucrose.

2) This is because **only one substrate will fit** into the active site.

3) The active site's **shape** is determined by the enzyme's **3D structure** (which is determined by the enzyme's **primary structure**).

4) Each **different enzyme** has a **different 3D structure** and so a **different shaped active site**. If the substrate shape doesn't match the active site, the reaction won't be catalysed.

5) If the 3D structure of a protein is **altered** in any way, the **shape** of the active site will **change**. This means the **substrate won't fit** into the active site and the enzyme will no longer be able to carry out its function.

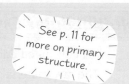

See p. 11 for more on primary structure.

Enzyme Concentration Affects the **Rate of Reaction**

1) The **more enzyme molecules** there are in a solution, the more likely a substrate molecule is to **collide** with one and form an **enzyme-substrate complex**. So increasing the concentration of the enzyme **increases** the **rate of reaction**.

2) But if the amount of **substrate** is **limited**, there comes a point when there's more than enough enzyme molecules to deal with all the available substrate, so adding more enzyme has **no further effect**.

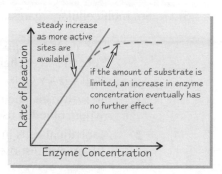

You Can **Measure** the **Initial Rate** of an **Enzyme-Controlled** Reaction

In the exam, you might be asked how to **investigate** the effect of **enzyme concentration** on the **initial rate of a reaction**. Here's one way you can do it:

Measure how fast the product of the reaction appears

You can do this by setting up an experiment like the one below — it shows **hydrogen peroxide** being broken down into **water** and **oxygen** by the **enzyme catalase**.

You can **measure** how much **oxygen** is given off (i.e. how much product is produced) with **different concentrations** of enzyme. Measure the amount of oxygen given off in the **first minute** of the reaction. Then **divide** the **volume** (in cm³) of oxygen produced by the **time** (in min), to get the **initial rate of reaction** (in cm³/min). The **more** oxygen that is given off in the first minute of the reaction, the **faster** the initial rate of reaction.

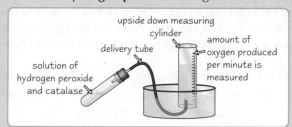

Practice Questions

Q1 What is an enzyme?

Q2 What is the name given to the amount of energy needed to start a reaction?

Exam questions

Q1 Explain how the specificity of enzymes is related to their 3D structure. [2 marks]

Q2 An experiment was carried out to find out the effect of increasing the enzyme concentration on the initial rate of a reaction. Using your knowledge, predict the outcome of the experiment and explain your answer. [4 marks]

<u>Porridge and two slices of toast — that's my activation energy...</u>

OK, nothing too tricky here. Enzymes basically catalyse loads of reactions in the body. And you can do a fancy experiment to measure the effect of changing enzyme concentration on the initial rate of a reaction (see the catalase reaction above). Make sure you know that increasing enzyme concentration only increases the rate of a reaction up to a certain point.

The Heart and Blood Vessels

The heart, along with various types of blood vessels, make up the circulatory system. Without this system, our cells wouldn't get the substances they need and waste substances wouldn't be removed from them.

Multicellular Organisms Need Mass Transport Systems

1) All cells **need energy** — most cells get energy via **aerobic respiration**.

2) The raw materials for this are **glucose** and **oxygen**, so the body has to make sure it can deliver enough of these to all its cells.

3) In single-celled organisms, these materials can **diffuse directly** into the cell across the cell membrane. The diffusion rate is quick because of the **short distance** the substances have to travel (see p. 30).

4) In **multicellular** organisms (like us), diffusion across the outer membrane would be **too slow** because of the **large distance** the substances would have to travel to reach **all** the cells — think of how far it is from your skin to your heart cells.

5) So, multicellular organisms have **mass transport systems**:

> 1) The **mass transport systems** are used to **carry raw materials** from specialised **exchange organs** (e.g. the lungs and the digestive system) to the body cells, and to **remove metabolic waste** (e.g. carbon dioxide).
>
> 2) In mammals, the mass transport system is the **circulatory system**, where **blood** is used to transport substances around the body.
>
> 3) Individual cells in tissues and organs get **nutrients** and **oxygen** from the blood and dispose of **metabolic waste** into the blood.

Richard had a different idea of mass transport from his biology teacher.

The Heart Pumps the Blood Around the Body

The heart keeps the blood moving so that substances can get **to** and **from** individual cells. You need to learn the structure of the heart. The **right side** pumps **deoxygenated blood** to the **lungs** and the **left side** pumps **oxygenated blood** to the **whole body**.
Note — the **left and right sides** are **reversed** on the diagram, cos it's the left and right of the person that the heart belongs to.

Each bit of the heart is adapted to do its job effectively.

1) The **left ventricle** of the heart has **thicker**, more muscular walls than the **right ventricle**, because it needs to contract powerfully to pump blood all the way round the body. The right side only needs to get blood to the lungs, which are nearby.

2) The **ventricles** have **thicker walls** than the **atria**, because they have to push blood out of the heart whereas the atria just need to push blood a short distance into the ventricles.

3) The **atrioventricular (AV) valves** link the atria to the ventricles and **stop blood flowing back** into the atria when the ventricles contract.

4) The **semi-lunar (SL) valves** link the ventricles to the pulmonary artery and aorta, and **stop blood flowing back** into the heart after the ventricles contract.

5) The **cords** attach the atrioventricular valves to the ventricles to stop them being forced up into the atria when the ventricles contract.

Internal Structure

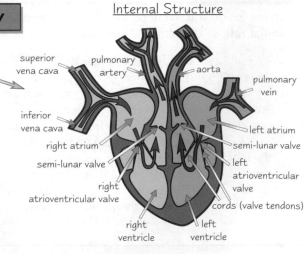

External Structure

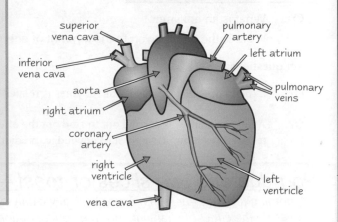

The Heart and Blood Vessels

Valves in the Heart Prevent Blood Flowing the Wrong Way

The **atrioventricular valves** link the atria to the ventricles, and the **semi-lunar** valves link the ventricles to the pulmonary artery and aorta — they stop blood flowing the **wrong way**. Here's how they work:

1) The **valves** only open one way — whether they're open or closed depends on the **relative pressure** of the heart chambers.

2) If there's higher pressure **behind** a valve, it's **forced open**.

3) If pressure is higher **in front** of the valve, it's **forced shut**.

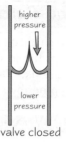

valve open   valve closed

Substances are Transported Around the Body in Blood Vessels

The heart pumps the blood around the body through the blood vessels. You need to know about **three** types of blood vessel — **arteries**, **veins** and **capillaries**. Read on...

1) **Arteries** carry blood from the heart **to the rest of the body**. They're thick-walled, **muscular** and have **elastic tissue** in the walls to cope with the **high pressure** caused by the heartbeat. The inner lining (**endothelium**) is **folded**, allowing the artery to **expand** — this also helps it to cope with high pressure.

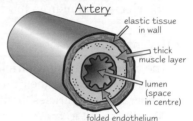

Artery

elastic tissue in wall

thick muscle layer

lumen (space in centre)

folded endothelium

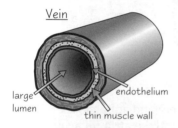

Vein

large lumen

endothelium

thin muscle wall

2) **Veins** take blood **back to the heart**. They're **wider** than equivalent arteries, with very little elastic or muscle tissue. Veins contain **valves** to stop the blood flowing backwards. Blood flow through the veins is helped by contraction of the **body muscles** surrounding them.

3) **Capillaries** are the **smallest** of the blood vessels. They are where **metabolic exchange** occurs — substances are **exchanged** between cells and the capillaries. There are networks of capillaries in tissue (called **capillary beds**), which **increase** the **surface area** for exchange. Capillary walls are only **one cell thick**, which speeds up **diffusion** of substances (e.g. glucose and oxygen) into and out of cells.

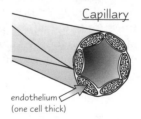

Capillary

endothelium (one cell thick)

Practice Questions

Q1 Why do multicellular organisms need mass transport systems?

Q2 Why is the left ventricle wall more muscular than the right ventricle wall?

Exam Questions

Q1 Explain how valves in the heart stop blood going back the wrong way. [6 marks]

Q2 Describe the structure of an artery and explain how it relates to its function. [4 marks]

Q3 Explain how the structure of capillaries enables them to carry out metabolic exchange efficiently. [4 marks]

If blood can handle transport this efficiently, the trains have no excuse...

Four hours I was waiting at the train station this weekend. Four hours! You may have noticed that biologists are obsessed with the relationship between structure and function, so whenever you're learning about the structure of something, make sure you know how this relates to its function. And what better place to start than arteries, veins and capillaries...

The Cardiac Cycle and Heart Rate

Now that you've seen all the bits that make up the cardiovascular system, it's time to see exactly what happens in your heart to make the blood flow — my heart's all of a flutter just thinking about it.

The **Cardiac Cycle** is the **Sequence** of Events in **One Heartbeat**

The cardiac cycle is an ongoing sequence of **contraction** (**systole**) and **relaxation** (**diastole**) of the atria and ventricles that keeps blood **continuously** circulating round the body. The **volume** of the atria and ventricles **changes** as they contract and relax. **Pressure** changes also occur, due to the changes in chamber volume (e.g. decreasing the volume of a chamber by contraction will increase the pressure of a chamber). The cardiac cycle can be simplified into three stages:

① Ventricular diastole, atrial systole

The **ventricles are relaxed**. The **atria contract**, decreasing the volume of the chamber and **increasing** the **pressure** inside the chamber. This **pushes** the blood into the ventricles. There's a slight **increase** in **ventricular pressure** and **chamber volume** as the **ventricles receive the ejected blood** from the contracting atria.

② Ventricular systole, atrial diastole

The **atria relax**. The **ventricles contract** (decreasing their volume), **increasing** their **pressure**. The pressure becomes **higher** in the ventricles than the atria, which forces the **AV valves shut** to prevent back-flow.
The **pressure** in the **ventricles is also higher than in the aorta and pulmonary artery**, which forces **open** the **SL valves** and blood is forced out into these arteries.

③ Ventricular diastole, atrial diastole

The **ventricles and the atria both relax**. The higher pressure in the pulmonary artery and aorta closes the SL valves to prevent back-flow into the ventricles. Blood returns to the heart and the **atria fill again** due to the higher pressure in the vena cava and pulmonary vein. In turn this starts to **increase** the **pressure** of the atria. As the ventricles continue to **relax**, their **pressure falls below the pressure of the atria** and so the **AV valves open**. This allows blood to flow **passively** (without being pushed by atrial contraction) into the ventricles from the atria. The atria contract, and the whole process begins again.

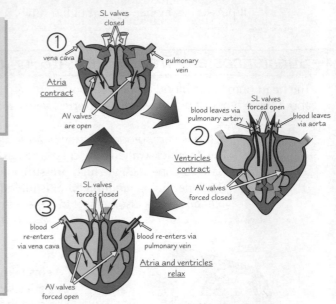

You Can **Investigate** the Effect of **Caffeine** on the **Heart Rate** of **Daphnia**

Daphnia are tiny aquatic **invertebrates**. They're **transparent**, so you can see their internal organs. This means it's pretty easy to monitor their **heart rate** (the **number of heartbeats** in a **minute**) by observing them through a **microscope**. Here's how you could investigate the effect of caffeine on their heart rate:

There's more on controls on page 78.

1) Make up a **range** of caffeine solutions of **different concentrations** and a **control** solution that has no caffeine in it at all.

2) Transfer **one** *Daphnia* into the dimple on a **cavity slide** (a microscope slide with a rounded dip).

3) Place the slide onto the stage of a **light microscope** and **focus** it on the beating heart of the *Daphnia*.

4) Place a small drop of **caffeine solution** onto the *Daphnia*.

5) **Count** the number of **heartbeats** in **10 seconds** and multiply this by **six** to calculate beats per minute (**heart rate**).

6) **Repeat** this 10 times using the **same concentration** of caffeine but a **different** *Daphnia* individual each time.

7) Don't forget to keep **all other factors constant** (e.g. temperature and volume of caffeine solution).

8) Repeat the experiment using the **other concentrations** of caffeine solution.

9) **Compare the results** to see how caffeine concentration affects heart rate, e.g. by drawing a graph (see next page).

The Cardiac Cycle and Heart Rate

Heart Rate *Increases* as Caffeine Concentration *Increases*

A good way to see the effect of caffeine concentration on heart rate is to draw a **graph** of the results of the *Daphnia* experiment.

1) Take the **average** of the 10 readings at each concentration and then graph your results — plot average heart rate (beats per minute) against concentration of caffeine.

2) Your results will look something like this. ⟶

3) The graph shows a **positive correlation** — as caffeine concentration **increases**, heart rate also **increases**.

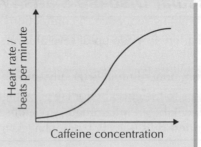

The result of the experiment — hooked on caffeine.

There are Some *Ethical Issues* Involved in Using *Invertebrates*

In the exam, you may have to discuss the **ethical issues** involved with using **invertebrates** in experiments. Here are some points to think about:

1) Experimenting on **animals** allows scientists to study things that would be **unethical** to study using humans.

2) But many people believe that using animals is **also unethical** — they can't give **consent** and they may be subjected to **painful procedures**.

3) Some people believe it's **more acceptable** to perform experiments on **invertebrates** (like *Daphnia*, spiders and insects) than on **vertebrates** (like dogs and monkeys).

4) This is because they're considered to be **simpler organisms** than vertebrates. For example, they have a much **less sophisticated nervous system**, which could mean that they feel less pain (or no pain). Also, invertebrates are more **distantly related** to humans than other vertebrates.

5) But there are still ethical issues to consider when experimenting with invertebrates. For example, some people believe it's unethical to cause **distress** or **suffering** to **any living organism** — e.g. by subjecting them to **extremes of temperature** or depriving them of **food**.

Practice Questions

Q1 What is: a) diastole, b) systole?

Q2 During ventricular systole, are the atrioventricular valves open or closed?

Q3 Why are the semi-lunar valves closed during ventricular and atrial diastole?

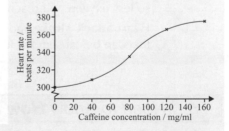

Exam Questions

Q1 Describe the pressure changes that occur in the heart during systole and diastole. [4 marks]

Q2 The graph shows the results of an experiment into the effects of caffeine on *Daphnia* heart rate.

a) Describe the results of the experiment. [1 mark]

b) Suggest two factors that would need to be kept constant during the experiment. [2 marks]

c) Suggest two reasons why some people may feel it's more acceptable to carry out experiments on invertebrates, such as *Daphnia*, than on vertebrates. [2 marks]

I reckon there are some ethical issues involved with sitting exams...

There's quite a mix of things to learn on these pages, but breathe deeply, slow your heart rate, and concentrate. Once you've got your head round the cardiac cycle, it's on to Daphnia. Make sure that you can outline how to set up the experiment and then put your debating hat on because it's time for some ethics.

Cardiovascular Disease

No, your heart won't break if HE/SHE (delete as appropriate) doesn't return your call... but there are diseases associated with the heart and blood vessels that you have to learn...

Most **Cardiovascular Disease** Starts With **Atheroma** Formation

1) The wall of an artery is made up of **several layers** (see page 15).

2) The **endothelium** (inner lining) is usually smooth and unbroken.

3) If **damage** occurs to the endothelium (e.g. by high blood pressure) there will be an **inflammatory response** — this is where **white blood cells** (mostly macrophages) move into the area.

4) These white blood cells and **lipids** (fats) from the blood, clump together under the endothelium to form **fatty streaks**.

5) Over time, **more white blood cells**, **lipids** and **connective tissue** build up and harden to form a **fibrous plaque** called an **atheroma**.

6) This plaque **partially blocks** the lumen of the **artery** and **restricts blood flow**, which causes **blood pressure** to **increase**.

7) The **hardening** of arteries, caused by atheromas, is called **atherosclerosis**.

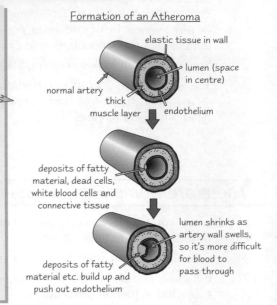

Formation of an Atheroma

elastic tissue in wall

lumen (space in centre)

normal artery

thick muscle layer   endothelium

deposits of fatty material, dead cells, white blood cells and connective tissue

lumen shrinks as artery wall swells, so it's more difficult for blood to pass through

deposits of fatty material etc. build up and push out endothelium

Atheromas Increase the **Risk** of **Thrombosis** in **Arteries**

1) As you know, **atheromas** develop within the **walls** of **arteries** (see above).

2) An atheroma can **rupture** (burst through) the **endothelium** of an artery, **damaging** the artery wall and leaving a **rough** surface.

3) This triggers **thrombosis** (blood clotting) — a **blood clot** forms at the **site** of the rupture (see below).

4) This blood clot can cause a complete **blockage** of the artery, or it can become **dislodged** and block a blood vessel elsewhere in the body.

5) The **blood flow** to **tissues** supplied by the blocked blood vessel will be severely **restricted**, so **less oxygen** will reach those tissues, resulting in damage.

6) **Heart attack**, **stroke** and **deep vein thrombosis** are three forms of **cardiovascular disease** that can be caused by blood clots — these are explained in more detail on the next page.

You Need to Know **How** a **Blood Clot Forms**

Thrombosis is used by the body to **prevent** lots of blood being **lost** when a **blood vessel** is **damaged**. A **series** of **reactions** occurs that leads to the formation of a **blood clot** (**thrombus**):

1) A **protein** called **thromboplastin** is **released** from the **damaged** blood vessel.

2) Thromboplastin triggers the **conversion** of **prothrombin** (a **soluble protein**) into **thrombin** (an **enzyme**).

3) Thrombin then catalyses the **conversion** of **fibrinogen** (a **soluble protein**) to **fibrin** (solid **insoluble fibres**).

4) The fibrin fibres **tangle together** and form a **mesh** in which **platelets** (**small fragments of cells** in the blood) and **red blood cells** get **trapped** — this forms the **blood clot**.

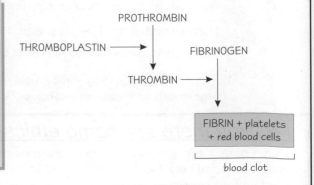

PROTHROMBIN

THROMBOPLASTIN ⟶

FIBRINOGEN

THROMBIN ⟶

FIBRIN + platelets + red blood cells

blood clot

Cardiovascular Disease

Blood Clots can Cause Heart Attacks...

1 The **heart muscle** is supplied with **blood** by the **coronary arteries**.

2 This blood contains the **oxygen** needed by heart muscle cells to carry out **respiration**.

3 If a coronary artery becomes **completely blocked** by a **blood clot** an area of the heart muscle will be totally **cut off** from its blood supply, so it **won't** receive any **oxygen**.

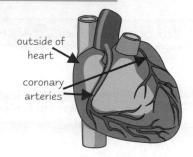

outside of heart

coronary arteries

4 This causes a **myocardial infarction** — more commonly known as a **heart attack**.

7 If **large areas** of the heart are affected complete **heart failure** can occur, which is often **fatal**.

6 **Symptoms** include **pain** in the chest and upper body, **shortness of breath** and **sweating**.

5 A heart attack can cause **damage** and **death** of the **heart muscle**.

...Stroke...

1) A **stroke** is a **rapid loss** of **brain function**, due to a **disruption** in the **blood supply** to the **brain**.

2) This can be caused by a **blood clot** in an **artery** leading to the brain, which **reduces** the amount of blood, and therefore **oxygen**, that can reach the brain.

...and Deep Vein Thrombosis

1) **Deep vein thrombosis** (DVT) is the formation of a **blood clot** in a **vein** deep inside the body — it usually happens in **leg veins**.

2) It can be caused by **prolonged inactivity**, e.g. during **long-haul flights**, and the risk **increases** with **age**.

Coronary Heart Disease (CHD) is Another Type of Cardiovascular Disease

Coronary heart disease (CHD) is when the **coronary arteries** have lots of **atheromas** in them, which restricts blood flow to the heart. The atheromas also increase the risk of **blood clots** forming, leading to an increased risk of heart attack.

Practice Questions

Q1 Describe how an atheroma forms.

Q2 What is the role of fibrin in the blood clotting process?

Exam Questions

Q1 Describe how atheromas can increase the risk of a person suffering from a heart attack. [5 marks]

Q2 Sufferers of a disorder called hypoprothrombinaemia have a reduced amount of prothrombin in their blood. Explain the likely effect this will have on their blood clotting mechanism. [3 marks]

Atherosclerosis, thrombosis — more like a spelling test than biology...

I know there's a lot to take in on these pages... but make sure you understand the link between atheromas, thrombosis and CVD — basically an atheroma forms, which can cause thrombosis, which can lead to CVD. Also, practise writing down the flow diagram of all the proteins involved in blood clotting, 'cause you need to know it in detail.

Risk Factors for Cardiovascular Disease

There are loads of factors that increase the risk of getting cardiovascular disease.
And you need to learn them all... unlucky...

Many **Factors** Can **Increase** the **Risk** of **Cardiovascular Disease (CVD)**

LIFESTYLE FACTORS:

1) **Diet** — a diet **high** in **saturated fat** increases the risk of CVD. This is because it **increases blood cholesterol level** (see next page), which **increases atheroma formation**. Atheromas can lead to the formation of **blood clots**, which can cause a **heart attack**, **stoke** or **DVT**.
A diet **high in salt** also increases the risk of CVD because it increases the risk of **high blood pressure** (see below).

2) **High blood pressure** — this **increases** the **risk** of **damage** to the **artery walls**, which **increases** the **risk** of **atheroma formation**, which can lead to CVD. **Excessive alcohol consumption**, **stress** and **diet** can **all** increase blood pressure.

3) **Smoking** —

   - **Carbon monoxide** in cigarette smoke combines with **haemoglobin** (the protein that carries oxygen in the blood) and **reduces** the amount of **oxygen** transported in the **blood**. This **reduces** the amount of **oxygen available to tissues**. If the heart muscle doesn't receive enough oxygen it can lead to a **heart attack** and if the brain doesn't receive enough oxygen it can lead to a **stroke**.

   - **Nicotine** in cigarette smoke makes **platelets sticky**, increasing the chance of **blood clots forming**, which increases the risk of CVD.

   - Smoking also **decreases** the **amount** of **antioxidants** in the blood — these are important for **protecting cells** from damage. Fewer antioxidants means **cell damage** in the **artery walls** is more likely, and this can lead to **atheroma formation**, which increases the risk of CVD.

4) **Inactivity** — a **lack** of **exercise** increases the risk of CVD because it **increases blood pressure** (see above).

FACTORS BEYOND YOUR CONTROL:

1) **Genetics** — some people inherit particular **alleles** (different versions of genes, see page 38) that make them **more likely** to have **high blood pressure** or **high blood cholesterol**, so they are **more likely** to suffer from CVD.

2) **Age** — the risk of developing CVD **increases with age**.

3) **Gender** — **men** are **three times more likely** to suffer from CVD than pre-menopausal women.

Perception of Risk Can be Different from **Actual Risk**

1) **Risk** can be defined as the **chance** of something **unfavourable** happening.
E.g. if you **smoke** you **increase** your chance of developing CVD.

2) The **statistical chance** of something unfavourable happening is supported by **scientific research**. E.g. the actual risk of **dying** from **CVD** is **60%** higher for smokers than for non-smokers.

3) People's **perception** of risk may be very **different** from the actual risk:

   - People may **overestimate** the risk — they may believe things to be a **greater risk** than they actually are. E.g. they may have **known someone** who **smoked** and **died** from CVD, and therefore think that if you smoke you **will** die of CVD. Also, there are often **articles** in the **media** about health issues, e.g. articles that highlight the link between smoking and CVD. **Constant exposure** to information like this can make people **constantly worry** that they'll get CVD.

   - Some people may **underestimate** the risk — they may believe things to be a **lower risk** than they actually are. This could be due to a **lack of information** making them **unaware** of the **factors** that contribute to diseases like CVD.

Melvin underestimated the risk of letting his mum dress him...

Risk Factors for Cardiovascular Disease

High Blood Cholesterol Increases the Risk of CVD

1) **Cholesterol** is a **lipid** made in the body.

2) Some is **needed** for the body to **function normally**.

3) Cholesterol needs to be attached to **protein** to be moved around, so the body forms **lipoproteins** — substances composed of both **protein** and **lipid**. There are **two types** of lipoprotein:

HIGH DENSITY LIPOPROTEINS (HDLs)

1) They are **mainly protein**.

2) They transport **cholesterol** from **body tissues** to the **liver** where it's **recycled** or **excreted**.

3) Their function is to **reduce total blood cholesterol** when the level is **too high**.

LOW DENSITY LIPOPROTEINS (LDLs)

1) They are **mainly lipid**.

2) They transport cholesterol from the **liver** to the **blood**, where it circulates until needed by cells.

3) Their function is to **increase total blood cholesterol** when the level is **too low**.

4) **High total blood cholesterol level** (the level of HDL, LDL and other cholesterol) and **high LDL level** have both been linked to an **increased risk** of **CVD**.

You May Have to Interpret Data on the Link Between Cholesterol and CVD

Take a look at the following example of the sort of study you might see in your **exam**:

There's more on interpreting data on pages 76-78.

The graph below shows the results of a study involving **27 939 American women**. The **LDL cholesterol level** was **measured** for each woman. These women were then **followed** for an average of **8 years** and the **occurrence** of **cardiovascular events** (heart attack, stroke or surgery on coronary arteries) or **death** from cardiovascular diseases was **recorded**. The **relative risk** of a cardiovascular event, **adjusted** for **other factors** that can affect CVD, was then calculated. Here are some of the things you might be asked to do:

1) **Describe the data** — The **relative risk** of a cardiovascular event **increases** as the level of **LDL** cholesterol **increases**.

2) **Draw conclusions** — The graph shows a **positive correlation** between the relative **risk** of a cardiovascular event and the level of **LDL cholesterol** in the blood (as one factor **increases**, the other **increases**).

3) **Check any conclusions are valid** — Be careful that any conclusions **match** the data, e.g. this data only looked at **women** — no males were involved, so you can't say that this trend is true for **everyone**. Also, you can't say that a high LDL cholesterol level is **correlated with** an increased risk of **heart attacks**, because the data shows **all** first cardiovascular events, including stroke and surgery.

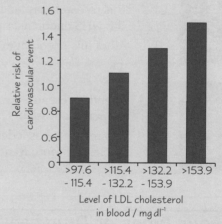

Practice Questions

Q1 Describe why high blood pressure increases the risk of CVD.

Q2 Give one reason why a person may overestimate the risk of developing CVD.

Exam Questions

Q1 Explain how smoking can increase the risk of developing CVD. [11 marks]

Q2 Explain the difference between high density lipoproteins (HDLs) and low density lipoproteins (LDLs). [6 marks]

Revision — a risk factor for headache, stress, boredom...

With all this scientific knowledge nowadays, you'd think that we'd have a better perception of risk. But some people still drive really fast even though it increases the risk of having an accident, and some people are terrified of going on a plane even though the actual risk of it crashing is very, very, very low. In fact, you should be more worried about passing your exams...

Prevention and Treatment of CVD

It's not all doom and gloom though — there are some changes you can make to your lifestyle to reduce your risk of developing CVD. And even if you get CVD there are treatments available.

Lifestyle Advice to Reduce the Risk of CVD is Based on Scientific Research

There've been loads of **scientific studies** carried out to **identify risk factors** (see pages 20-21) for CVD.
The **results** from these scientific studies are published in **scientific journals**.
Government organisations (like the **NHS**) and the **media** report the findings to the **general public**.
People can use this information to **make choices** about their **lifestyle**, so they can **reduce** their chance of developing CVD.

EXAMPLE: DIET

1) Scientific research has linked a **diet high in saturated fat** to an **increased risk** of CVD.
   - This information can be used to **educate people** about the risk of **certain diets** and to encourage them to **reduce** their saturated fat intake.
   - The **Food Standards Agency** encourages **food manufacturers** to label their products to show the amount of **saturated fat** in them, so people can make an **informed choice** about what they eat.
2) Scientific studies have also shown that **obese** people are **more likely** to develop CVD.
   - **Obesity indicators**, like BMI (**body mass index**), can be used to assess if people are **overweight** or **obese**. If someone is overweight or obese, then that person can make **choices** to **reduce** their **weight** and reduce their **risk of CVD** — e.g. they may go on a **diet** or **increase** their **activity level**. These obesity indicators can then be used to **monitor** the **effects** any **changes in lifestyle** have on the person's weight.

EXAMPLE: SMOKING

1) Scientific research has linked **smoking** to an **increased risk** of CVD (see page 20).
2) This research has led to **TV adverts** and **warnings** on **cigarette packets** about the risks of smoking. The NHS encourages people to give up by giving **free advice** and **prescribing nicotine patches**.
3) All of this encourages people to **stop** smoking and so reduce their risk of CVD.

EXAMPLE: EXERCISE

1) Scientific research has linked **inactivity** to an **increased risk** of CVD (see page 20).
2) This research has led to campaigns that encourage people to **exercise more frequently** to reduce their risk of CVD.

Not allowing sweets has been linked to an increased risk of tantrums...

Four Types of Drug can be used to Treat CVD

Although **prevention** is **better** than **cure**, there are some **treatments** for CVD.
You need to know **how** four of them work and be able to **describe** their **benefits and risks**.

(1) Antihypertensives Reduce High Blood Pressure

These drugs include **diuretics** (which cause **more urine** to be produced, so **reduce** the volume of **blood**), **beta-blockers** (which **reduce** the **strength** of the **heartbeat**) and **vasodilators** (which **widen** the **blood vessels**). All of these **reduce blood pressure**, so there's **less chance** of **damage** occurring to the walls of the arteries. This **reduces** the risk of **atheromas** forming and **blood clots** developing (see p. 19).

1) **Benefits** — The **different types** of antihypertensives work in **different ways**, so they can be given in **combination** to reduce blood pressure. Also, blood pressure can be **monitored at home**, so the patient can see if the drugs are **working**.
2) **Risks** — **Palpitations** (rapid beating of the heart), **abnormal heart rhythms, fainting, headaches** and **drowsiness** are all side effects of these drugs caused by the **blood pressure** becoming **too low**. Other side effects include **allergic reactions** and **depression**.

Prevention and Treatment of CVD

2) Plant Statins Reduce Cholesterol in the Blood

Plants contain chemicals called **stanols** and **sterols**. These **reduce blood cholesterol** in humans by **reducing** the amount of cholesterol **absorbed** from the **gut**. They're often referred to as **plant statins** (statins are a type of drug that lower cholesterol, but they work in a different way). A lower blood cholesterol level **reduces atheroma formation**, which reduces the risk of CVD. To consume enough plant statins to affect your blood cholesterol you'd have to eat **loads** of plants though. But, you can buy **foods** with **added plant statins** if you want, e.g. some margarines.

1) **Benefits** — Statins reduce the risk of **developing CVD**.
2) **Risks** — They can **reduce** the **absorbtion** of some **vitamins** from the gut.

3) Anticoagulants Reduce the Formation of Blood Clots

Anticoagulants (e.g. warfarin and heparin) **reduce blood clotting**.
This means blood clots are **less likely** to form at sites of **damage** in artery walls.
So there's **less chance** of a **blood vessel** becoming **blocked** by a blood clot (see p. 19), reducing the risk of CVD.

1) **Benefits** — Anticoagulants can be used to treat people who **already have blood clots** or **CVD** — they **prevent** any existing blood clots from **growing any larger** and prevent any **new** blood clots from **forming**. However, anticoagulants **can't get rid** of **existing** blood clots.
2) **Risks** — If a person taking these drugs is badly **injured**, the reduction in blood clotting can cause **excessive bleeding**, which can lead to **fainting** (and in serious cases **death**). Other side effects include **allergic reactions**, **osteoporosis** (weakened bones) and **swelling** of the tissues. These drugs can also **damage** the **fetus** if they're taken during pregnancy.

4) Platelet Inhibitory Drugs Also Reduce the Formation of Blood Clots

Platelet inhibitory drugs (e.g. **aspirin**) are a type of **anticoagulant** (see above).
They work by **preventing platelets clumping together** to form a blood clot.
So, they **reduce** the formation of **blood clots**, reducing the chance of a blood vessel becoming **blocked** by a clot.

1) **Benefits** — As with anticoagulants, these can be used to treat people who **already have blood clots** or **CVD**.
2) **Risks** — Side effects include **rashes**, **diarrhoea**, **nausea**, **liver function problems** and **excessive bleeding**, especially after a serious injury (see above).

Practice Questions

Q1 Why are obesity indicators useful?
Q2 Describe two risks involved in taking platelet inhibitory drugs.

Exam Question

Q1 A patient who is at risk of developing coronary heart disease (CHD) goes to see his doctor.
The patient is obese and suffers from high blood pressure.

a) Suggest a type of drug the doctor could prescribe to treat the patient's high blood pressure. Explain how the drug reduces the risk of CHD and give one disadvantage of taking it. [4 marks]

b) Suggest two lifestyle changes that the doctor may recommend to his patient to reduce his risk of developing CHD. [2 marks]

The only lifestyle advice I take is from Trinny & Susannah...

*It's better to prevent CVD in the first place, rather than having to take a cocktail of drugs to treat it.
Also, these drugs don't cure the problem — they don't get rid of existing atheromas or blood clots, they just prevent them from getting any worse. Right, so I'll meet you down at the park in about ten mins for a quick sprint...*

Interpreting Data on Risk Factors

Those pesky examiners may ask you to analyse data on risk factors for other diseases too... do they know no limit?

You May Have to **Analyse** and **Interpret Data** About **Illness** or **Mortality**

In the **exam** you might have to analyse illness or mortality data (for any disease) to determine if something is a **risk factor**. To get you in the mood, here's one I prepared earlier:

STUDY ONE

A study was carried out to analyse data, gathered from **53 studies worldwide**, about the **link** between **smoking** and **breast cancer**. The study looked at **22 255** women **with** breast cancer and **40 832** women **without** breast cancer, all of whom reported **drinking no alcohol**. The results below show the **relative risk** of breast cancer for women with **different smoking histories**.

There's more on interpreting data on pages 76-78.

Here are some of the things you might be asked to do:

1) <u>Describe the data</u> — The results show that the **relative risk** of breast cancer for women who don't drink alcohol is **similar regardless of smoking history**.

2) <u>Draw conclusions</u> — The results show that for women who don't drink alcohol, smoking is **not associated** with an **increased risk** of breast cancer.

3) <u>Check any conclusions are valid</u> — This data appears to show **no link** between smoking history and the relative risk of breast cancer in women who don't drink, but you **can't** say that smoking **doesn't affect** breast cancer risk at all. The data **doesn't** take into account women who drink. Smoking and alcohol **together** could **affect the risk** of breast cancer. Also, the study doesn't take into account **other factors** that could affect risk of breast cancer such as the use of **hormone replacement treatment**, **physical activity**, etc.

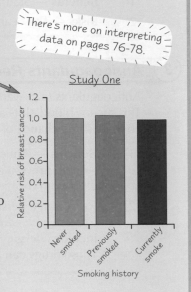

You Need to be Able to **Recognise Conflicting Evidence**

1) The **evidence** from **one study** alone **wouldn't usually be enough** to conclude that a factor is a **health risk**.

2) **Similar studies** would be carried out to investigate the link. If these studies came to the **same conclusion**, the conclusion would become **increasingly accepted**.

3) Sometimes studies come up with **conflicting evidence** though — evidence that leads to a **different conclusion** than other studies. For example, one study may conclude that a factor <u>isn't</u> **a health risk**, whereas another study may conclude that the **same** factor <u>is</u> **a health risk**:

STUDY TWO

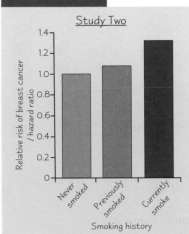

A study was carried out to determine if smoking is linked to an increased risk of breast cancer. **116 544** women without breast cancer in **California** were sent **questionnaires** to establish their **smoking history** and other personal information. The women were then followed for **5 years**. The results on the left show the **relative risk of breast cancer**, **adjusted** for **other factors** such as age and alcohol consumption, for women with **different smoking histories**.

1) <u>Describe the data</u> — The results show that the **relative risk** of breast cancer for women in California is **higher** for women who **previously smoked** or **still smoke** compared to those who have never smoked.

2) <u>Draw conclusions</u> — The results show that for women in California, smoking **is associated** with an **increased risk** of breast cancer.

3) <u>Comment on the conflicting evidence</u> — This second study shows that smoking **is linked** to an increased risk of breast cancer, which **conflicts** with the evidence from **study one** (see above). Because the two studies have produced conflicting evidence, **more results** would be needed in order to **fully assess** if smoking is an **important health risk** for the development of **breast cancer**.

Interpreting Data on Risk Factors

You May Have to *Evaluate* the *Design* of *Studies*

In the **exam** you could be asked to **evaluate** the **design** of a study they've given you. Here are some things to look out for:

1) **Sample size** — the **greater** the number of people used in a study, the **more reliable** the results.

2) **Variables** — the **more variables** (other factors that could affect the results) that have been **controlled** in a study, the **more reliable** the results.

3) **Data collection** — the **less bias** involved in collecting the data, the **more reliable** the results.

4) **Controls** — the presence of controls **increases** the reliability of the results.

5) **Repetition** by other scientists — if other scientists produce the **same results**, then the results are **more reliable**.

Reliable results are more likely to be true.

See pages 76-78 for loads more on evaluating data.

EXAMPLE: STUDY ONE

1) **Sample size** — The study had a **large** sample size of **63 087 women** in total, which is good.

2) **Variables** — The study didn't take into account **some variables** that can affect the risk of breast cancer, like **hormone replacement therapy** and **physical activity**. This could have affected the results (decreasing their reliability).

3) **Data collection** — The data was collected from **53 other studies** but we don't know how those other studies were designed.

4) **Controls** — There were a large number of controls, **40 832 women**. This increases the reliability of the results.

5) **Repetition by other scientists** — Study two **doesn't agree** with the conclusion of study one.

EXAMPLE: STUDY TWO

1) **Sample size** — This study had a **really large** sample size of **116 544 women**, which is good.

2) **Variables** — This study took into account **other variables** like **hormone replacement therapy**, **physical activity**, alcohol consumption, etc. This **increases** the **reliability** of the results.

3) **Data collection** — The data was collected from **questionnaires**, which can be biased. This **decreases** the **reliability** of the results.

4) **Repetition by other scientists** — Study one **doesn't agree** with the conclusion of study two.

Practice Questions

Q1 What is meant by conflicting evidence?

Q2 Why is it important to look at the data collection method when evaluating study design?

Exam Question

Q1 A study was carried out involving 34 439 male British doctors. Questionnaires were used to find out the smoking habits of the doctors. The number of deaths among the participants from ischaemic heart disease (coronary heart disease) was counted, and adjustments were made to account for differences in age. The graph on the right shows the results.

a) Describe the trend shown by the graph.

[1 mark]

b) Use the information provided to evaluate the study design.

[3 marks]

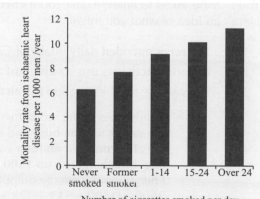

Exams — definitely a health risk...

These evaluating evidence questions come up quite a lot at AS level. The examiners like to see that you can analyse the data and that you can pick out the good and bad bits of a study. Luckily, I'm giving you plenty of examples of these types of questions. Make sure you look at the section at the back of this book on how to interpret data — then you'll be sorted.

Diet and Energy

Obesity is a risk factor for CVD (and other diseases), so it's important to maintain a healthy weight. Weight is affected by your diet as well as how much energy you use doing things like playing video games and stealing traffic cones...

Organisms Take In and Use Up Energy

Henri knew the cheese would push him over budget — but what harm could it do?

1) Organisms need a **supply** of **energy**, so that they can **grow**, **move**, **reproduce** etc. — in animals this energy is provided in the form of **food**.

2) **Energy budget** is a term used to describe the **amount of energy taken in** by an organism (in food) **and** the amount of energy **used up** by an organism (e.g. by moving).

Energy Imbalance Causes Changes in Weight

Ideally, a person should **take in** the **same amount** of energy as **they use up** — their energy budget should be **balanced**. If there's an **imbalance** in the energy budget, it will **affect** the **person's weight**:

WEIGHT GAIN

1) If energy **intake** is **higher** than energy **output**, the **excess energy** will be turned into **fat reserves** by the body, so the person will **gain weight**.

2) For example, if a person **consumes** food containing **4000 Calories** a day and carries out **activities** that burn **3000 Calories** a day, there'll be an **excess** of **1000 Calories** per day, so they'll put on weight.

3) If the energy difference is **a lot** and it's **sustained** over a **long period** of time, the person could become **obese**.

WEIGHT LOSS

1) If energy **intake** is **lower** than energy **output**, the body will have to **get** more energy from somewhere — it'll **turn** some of its **fat reserves** into energy, so the person will **lose weight**.

2) For example, if a person **consumes** food containing **2500 Calories** a day but carries out **activities** that burn **3000 Calories** a day, they will have an energy **deficit** of **500 Calories** per day, so they'll lose weight.

3) If this energy difference is **large** and is **sustained** over a **long period** of time, the person is likely to become **underweight**.

You May Have to Analyse Data on Energy Budgets and Diet

You may be asked to analyse data about **energy budgets** (input and output) in the exam. Here's an idea of what you might get:

1) The **recommended daily intake** of Calories is **2000** for **women** and **2500** for **men**.

2) **Different activities** use up **different amounts** of Calories, as shown in the table.

3) You can use this information to **calculate** people's **energy budgets**:

Activity	Number of Calories used per hour
Cooking	159
Dog walking	224
Gardening	328
Swimming	513

You need to multiply these figures by the number of hours the activity lasts.

- Ranjit takes in the recommended daily intake of Calories a day (**2500**). He swims for **one hour** and does **one hour** of **gardening** each day. He also **cooks** for **an hour** each day. His **bodily functions** (e.g. breathing) use up **1500** Calories per day. So his energy budget is:
Energy input – energy output = energy budget
2500 – (1500 + 513 + 328 + 159) = **0**
Ranjit's energy budget is **balanced** — he takes in as much as he uses up.

- Christina takes in **2000** Calories a day. She **walks the dog** for **an hour** every **morning** and every **night**. Her **bodily functions** use up **1200** Calories per day. So her energy budget is:
Energy input – energy output = energy budget
2000 – (1200 + 224 + 224) = **352 Calories**
Christina has an **excess** of **352 Calories** per day.

Diet and Energy

You Can *Measure* the *Amount* of *Vitamin C* in Your *Food*

1) You need to be able to **describe** how to carry out an **experiment** to find out **how much vitamin C** is in a **food sample**.

2) This can be done using a chemical called **DCPIP** — a **blue** dye that turns **colourless** in the presence of vitamin C.

Here's how you do it:

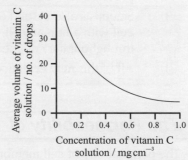

Melanie was the same colour as her orange juice but had less vitamin C content.

First you need to make a calibration curve. To do this you need to:

1) Make up several **vitamin C solutions** of **different, known concentrations**, (e.g. 10 mg/cm³, 20 mg/cm³, 30 mg/cm³). Ideally, you need about **six** different solutions.

2) Measure out a **set volume** of DCPIP (at a **set concentration**) into a test tube.

3) **Add** one of the **vitamin C solutions** to the DCPIP, **drop by drop**, using a pipette.

4) Gently **shake** the test tube for a **set length of time** after each drop of vitamin C solution is added.

5) When the solution turns **colourless**, **record** the **volume** (no. of drops) of vitamin C solution that has been added.

6) **Repeat** the experiment **twice more**, with the **same** solution, and take an **average** of the three readings.

7) Make sure you keep **all** the other **variables** constant during the experiment, e.g. temperature.

8) **Repeat** the above procedure with **each solution**.

9) Use the results to make a **line graph**, showing volume of vitamin C solution against its concentration — this is the **calibration curve**.

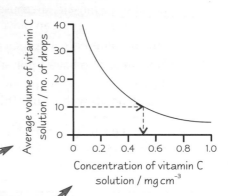

Then you can test the **unknown solution** in the same way as the known concentrations and use the calibration curve to find its concentration. E.g. 10 drops of an **unknown solution** is needed to turn DCPIP colourless. Reading **across** the calibration curve from a volume of **10 drops** shows that the concentration of vitamin C in the unknown solution is **0.5 mg/cm³**.

Practice Questions

Q1 What is an energy budget?

Q2 Explain how an energy imbalance causes weight gain.

Exam Questions

Q1 The graph on the right shows a calibration curve for vitamin C concentration.

a) 25 drops of DCPIP were needed to turn a vitamin C solution of unknown concentration colourless. Use the calibration curve to work out the concentration of the solution. Show your working on the graph. [2 marks]

b) Suggest three variables that should be kept constant in an experiment like this. [3 marks]

Q2 A woman takes in 2000 Calories a day in food. She needs 1200 Calories each day to maintain her basic bodily functions. She also swims for two hours and does two hours of gardening.

a) Use the table on page 26 to calculate her energy budget and explain what short-term effect this energy budget will have on her weight. [3 marks]

b) If the woman sustained this energy budget over a long period of time, what effect would it have on her weight? [1 mark]

Eat beans to increase the amount of Calories used for bodily functions...

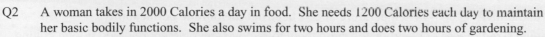

If you've done an hour's revision you've used up around 120 Calories (which is 90 more than you'd use just sat on your bum watching telly)... well done you — go and have a biscuit to celebrate (and even up your energy balance).

Cell Membrane Structure

The cell membrane is basically the cell boundary. To understand how substances get across this boundary (so they can enter or leave the cell) you have to know its structure. All I can say is... this section does get better.

Cell Membranes have a 'Fluid Mosaic' Structure

The **structure** of all membranes is basically the same. They're composed of **lipids** (mainly phospholipids — a type of lipid with a phosphate group attached to it), **proteins** and **carbohydrates** (usually attached to proteins or lipids).

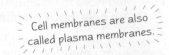
Cell membranes are also called plasma membranes.

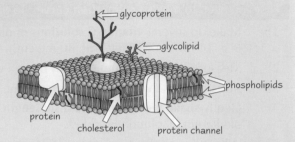

1)   In 1972, the **fluid mosaic model** was suggested to describe the **arrangement** of **molecules** in the membrane.

2)   In the model, **phospholipid molecules** form a continuous, double layer (**bilayer**). This bilayer is '**fluid**' because the phospholipids are **constantly moving**.

3)   **Protein molecules** are scattered through the bilayer, like tiles in a **mosaic**. Because the phospholipid bilayer is fluid, the proteins can **move around** within it.

4)   Some **proteins** have a **polysaccharide** (carbohydrate) **chain** attached — these are called **glycoproteins**.

5)   Some **lipids** also have a **polysaccharide chain** attached — these are called **glycolipids**.

6)   **Cholesterol** (a type of lipid) is also present in the membrane. It fits **in between** the **phospholipids**, forming **bonds** with them. This makes the membrane more **rigid**.

The membrane is **partially permeable** — **small molecules** can move through **gaps** between the **phospholipids**, but **large molecules** and **ions** can only pass through special **membrane proteins** called **channel proteins** and **carrier proteins** (see page 32).

The Fluid Mosaic Model is Based on Scientific Evidence

Electron microscopes show more detail than light microscopes.

1)   Before the 1970s, most scientists believed cell membranes were composed of a **phospholipid layer** between **two continuous layers of proteins**. This was because **electron microscope** (EM) **images** appeared to show **three layers** in a cell membrane.

2)   In time, **improved** EM techniques showed a **bilayer** of phospholipids, and **new methods** for **analysing proteins** showed that they were **randomly distributed** in cell membranes, not in a continuous layer.

3)   Scientists also carried out experiments that proved the cell membrane is **fluid** — e.g. they fused a **mouse cell** with a **human cell**, and found that the mouse and human **membrane proteins** completely **intermixed** throughout the cell membrane — the proteins could only **mix** like this if the membrane was fluid.

4)   All of this **new evidence** led to the **fluid mosaic model**.

The Permeability of the Cell Membrane can be Investigated in the Lab

The permeability of cell membranes is affected by **different conditions**, e.g. **temperature** and **alcohol concentration**. You can investigate how these things affect permeability by doing an experiment using **beetroot**. Beetroot cells contain a **coloured pigment** that **leaks out** — the **higher** the **permeability** of the membrane, the **more pigment** leaks out of the cell.

Here's how you could investigate how **temperature** affects **beetroot membrane permeability**:

1)   Cut five **equal sized** pieces of beetroot and **rinse** them to remove any pigment released during cutting.

2)   Place the five pieces in five different **test tubes**, each with **5 cm³ of water**.

3)   Place each test tube in a **water bath** at a **different temperature**, e.g. 10 °C, 20 °C, 30 °C, 40 °C, 50 °C, for the **same length of time**.

4)   **Remove** the pieces of beetroot from the tubes, leaving just the **coloured liquid**.

5)   Now you need to use a **colorimeter** — a machine that passes **light** through the liquid and measures how much of that light is **absorbed**. The **higher** the absorbance, the **more pigment released**, so the **higher** the **permeability** of the membrane.

Cell Membrane Structure

Increasing the Temperature Increases Membrane Permeability

Experiments like the one on the previous page have shown that membrane permeability **changes** with temperature:

(1) **Temperatures below 0 °C**
The phospholipids don't have much energy, so they can't move very much. They're **packed closely together** and the membrane is **rigid**. But **channel proteins** and **carrier proteins** in the membrane **deform**, **increasing** the **permeability** of the membrane. **Ice crystals** may form and **pierce** the membrane making it **highly permeable** when it thaws.

(2) **Temperatures between 0 and 45 °C**
The phospholipids can **move** around and **aren't** packed as tightly together — the membrane is **partially permeable**. As the temperature **increases** the phospholipids **move more** because they have more energy — this **increases** the **permeability** of the membrane.

(3) **Temperatures above 45 °C**
The phospholipid bilayer starts to **melt** (break down) and the membrane becomes more **permeable**. **Water** inside the cell **expands**, putting pressure on the membrane. **Channel proteins** and **carrier proteins deform** so they can't control what enters or leaves the cell — this increases the **permeability** of the membrane.

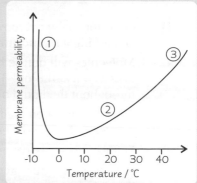

Increasing the Alcohol Concentration Increases Membrane Permeability

1) You can also test the effect of **alcohol concentration** on **membrane permeability** — the graph on the right shows the results you'd expect to get.

2) As alcohol concentration **increases**, the permeability of the cell membrane **increases**.

3) This is because alcohol **dissolves** the **lipids** in the cell membrane, so the membrane **loses** its **structure**.

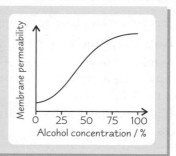

Practice Questions

Q1 How are phospholipids arranged in a cell membrane?

Q2 Why can proteins move around in the membrane?

Q3 What happens to the permeability of a cell membrane as the temperature increases?

Exam Question

Q1 The table on the right shows the results of an investigation into the effect of alcohol concentration on the permeability of beetroot cell membranes.

a) Suggest a suitable method that could have been used to obtain these results. [5 marks]

b) What conclusion can be drawn from the results? [1 mark]

c) Suggest an explanation for the results. [2 marks]

Alcohol concentration / %	Absorbance
0	0.14
25	0.22
50	0.49
75	1.03
100	1.28

Perm-eability — it's definitely decreased since the 80s...

Scientists are a bit annoying — they keep changing their minds about things like the structure of the cell membrane. But they don't do it on a whim — they need new experimental data that proves something isn't how they thought it was.

Transport Across the Cell Membrane

Some substances can cross the cell membrane without using energy — this is called passive transport. It's pretty handy for things like gas exchange and water movement.

Diffusion is the Passive Movement of Particles

1) Diffusion is the net movement of particles (molecules or ions) from an area of **higher concentration** to an area of **lower concentration**.

2) Molecules will diffuse **both ways**, but the **net movement** will be to the area of **lower concentration**. This continues until particles are **evenly distributed** throughout the liquid or gas.

3) The **concentration gradient** is the path from an area of higher concentration to an area of lower concentration. Particles diffuse **down** a concentration gradient.

4) Diffusion is a **passive process** — **no energy** is needed for it to happen.

5) Particles can diffuse **across cell membranes**, as long as they can **move freely** through the membrane. E.g. oxygen and carbon dioxide molecules are **small enough** to pass easily through spaces between phospholipids.

Diffusion — not good in a swimming pool.

Gas Exchange Surfaces are Adapted for Efficient Diffusion

All living organisms **respire** — they **take in oxygen** and **give out carbon dioxide**. These gases **diffuse** across a surface called the **gas exchange surface**.

Most gas exchange surfaces have two things in common:

1) They have a **large surface area**.

2) They're **thin** (often just one layer of epithelial cells) — this provides a **short diffusion pathway** across the gas exchange surface.

All these features **increase** the **rate of diffusion**.

The organism also maintains a **steep concentration gradient** of gases across the exchange surface.

The rate of diffusion also increases with temperature because the molecules have more kinetic energy — they move faster.

The Lungs are Adapted for Efficient Gaseous Exchange

In mammals the gas exchange surface is the **alveolar epithelium** in the **lungs**:

1) **Oxygen** diffuses **out of** the alveoli, across the **alveolar epithelium** (a layer of thin, flat cells) and the **capillary endothelium** (a type of epithelium that forms the capillary wall), and into the **blood**.

2) **Carbon dioxide** diffuses **into** the alveoli from the blood and is **breathed out**.

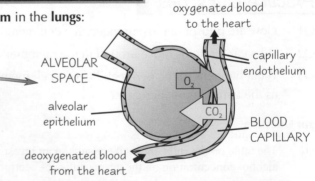

The mammalian lungs have the following features, which all help to **increase** the **rate** of **gas exchange**:

1) **Many alveoli** provide a **large surface area** for diffusion to occur across.

2) The **alveolar epithelium** and **capillary endothelium** are each only **one cell thick**, giving a **short diffusion pathway**.

3) All the alveoli have a **good blood supply** from capillaries — they constantly **take away oxygen** and **bring more carbon dioxide**, maintaining the **concentration gradient**.

4) **Breathing in and out** refreshes the air in the alveoli, keeping the **concentration gradients** high.

Transport Across the Cell Membrane

Osmosis is the Diffusion of Water Molecules

1) Osmosis is the **diffusion** of **water molecules** across a **partially permeable membrane**, from an area of **higher concentration** to an area of **lower concentration**.

2) Water molecules will diffuse **both ways** through the membrane, but the **net movement** will be to the side with the **lower concentration** of water molecules.

Partially permeable membranes can be useful at sea.

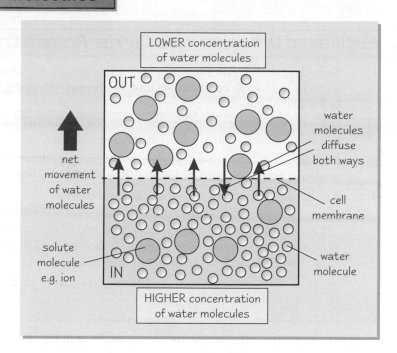

Practice Questions

Q1 Diffusion is a passive process. What does this mean?

Q2 What is osmosis?

Exam Questions

Q1 Efficient gas exchange surfaces have the following characteristics:

- large surface area
- short diffusion pathway
- high concentration gradient

Explain how these characteristics apply to human lungs. [5 marks]

Q2 Pieces of potato of equal mass were put into different concentrations of sucrose solution for three days. The difference in mass for each is recorded in the table on the right.

Concentration of sucrose / %	1	2	3	4
Mass difference / g	0.4	0.2	0	– 0.2

a) Explain why the pieces of potato in 1% and 2% sucrose solutions gained mass. [3 marks]

b) Suggest a reason why the mass of the piece of potato in 3% sucrose solution stayed the same. [1 mark]

c) What would you expect the mass difference for a potato in a 5% solution to be? Explain your answer. [4 marks]

All these molecules moving about — you'd think they'd get tired...

Right, so if you're a small molecule you can cross the membrane by simple diffusion, e.g. oxygen and carbon dioxide are small enough to diffuse through gaps between phospholipids in the membranes of alveolar epithelial cells. And if you're a water molecule you can also cross the membrane by diffusion, but it has a fancy name — osmosis. Got it.

Transport Across the Cell Membrane

Facilitated diffusion is another passive transport process, but there's also an active transport process, which is imaginatively named 'active transport'. Facilitated diffusion and active transport are actually quite similar though — they both involve proteins.

Facilitated Diffusion uses Carrier Proteins and Protein Channels

1) Some **larger molecules** (e.g. amino acids, glucose) and **charged atoms** (e.g. chloride ions) **can't diffuse directly through** the phospholipid bilayer of the cell membrane.

2) Instead they diffuse through **carrier proteins** or **channel proteins** in the cell membrane — this is called **facilitated diffusion**.

3) Like diffusion, facilitated diffusion moves particles **down** a **concentration gradient**, from a higher to a lower concentration.

4) It's also a passive process — it **doesn't** use **energy**.

Andy needed all his concentration for this particular gradient...

Carrier proteins move **large molecules** into or out of the cell, down their concentration gradient. **Different carrier proteins** facilitate the diffusion of **different molecules**.

1) First, a large molecule **attaches** to a carrier protein in the membrane.

2) Then, the protein **changes shape**.

3) This **releases** the molecule on the **opposite side** of the membrane.

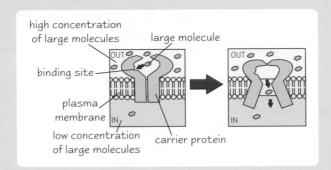

Channel proteins form **pores** in the membrane for **charged particles** to diffuse through (down their concentration gradient). **Different channel proteins** facilitate the diffusion of **different charged particles**.

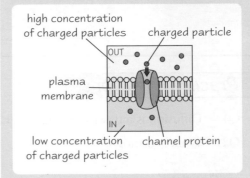

Active Transport Moves Substances Against a Concentration Gradient

Active transport uses **energy** to move **molecules** and **ions** across cell membranes, **against** a **concentration gradient**. This process also involves **carrier proteins**.

1) The process is pretty similar to facilitated diffusion — a molecule **attaches** to the carrier protein, the protein **changes shape** and this moves the molecule **across** the membrane, **releasing it** on the other side.

2) The only difference is that **energy** is used (from **ATP** — a common source of energy used in the cell), to move the solute against its concentration gradient.

3) The diagram on the right shows the active transport of **calcium**.

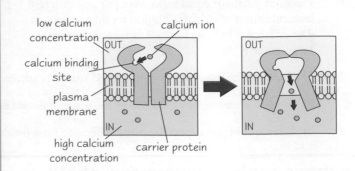

Transport Across the Cell Membrane

Cells can *Take in* Substances by *Endocytosis*

1) Some molecules are way too **large** to be taken into a cell by carrier proteins, e.g. proteins, lipids and some carbohydrates.

2) Instead a cell can **surround** a substance with a **section** of its **cell membrane**.

3) The membrane then **pinches off** to form a **vesicle** inside the cell containing the **ingested substance** — this is **endocytosis**.

4) Some cells take in much larger objects by endocytosis — for example, some **white blood cells** (called phagocytes) use endocytosis to take in things like **microorganisms** and **dead cells** so that they can destroy them.

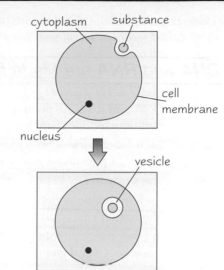

Cells can *Secrete* Substances by *Exocytosis*

1) Some substances **produced** by the cell (e.g. **digestive enzymes**, **hormones**, **lipids**) need to be **released** from the cell — this is done by **exocytosis**.

2) **Vesicles** containing these substances **pinch off** from the sacs of the **Golgi apparatus** (a structure that processes new proteins and lipids — see page 45) and **move towards** the cell membrane.

3) The vesicles **fuse** with the **cell membrane** and **release** their contents **outside** the cell.

4) Some substances (like membrane proteins) **aren't** released outside the cell — instead they are **inserted** straight into the cell membrane.

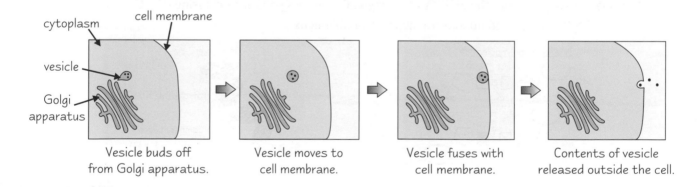

Vesicle buds off from Golgi apparatus. → Vesicle moves to cell membrane. → Vesicle fuses with cell membrane. → Contents of vesicle released outside the cell.

Practice Questions

Q1 What is active transport?

Q2 Which molecule provides the energy for active transport?

Exam Questions

Q1 Describe the role of membrane proteins in facilitated diffusion. [6 marks]

Q2 Explain the difference between endocytosis and exocytosis. [4 marks]

Revision — like working against a concentration gradient...

Wouldn't it be great if you could revise by endocytosis — you could just stick this book on your head and your brain would slowly surround it and take it in... actually when I put it like that it sounds a bit gross. Maybe just stick to good old 'closing the book and scribbling down the diagrams till you know them off by heart'.

Structure of DNA and Replication

*These pages are about the structure of **DNA** (**d**eoxyribo**n**ucleic **a**cid) and **RNA** (plain ol' **r**ibo**n**ucleic **a**cid), plus a little thing called semi-conservative replication, which is kinda important to us living things.*

DNA and RNA are Made from Mononucleotides

1) DNA and RNA are **polynucleotides** — they're made up of lots of **mononucleotides** (single nucleotides) joined together.

2) Each mononucleotide is made from a **pentose sugar** (with 5 carbon atoms), a **phosphate** group and a **nitrogenous base**.

3) The **sugar** in DNA is **d**eoxyribose sugar and in RNA it's **r**ibose sugar.

4) Each mononucleotide has the **same sugar and phosphate**. The **base** on each mononucleotide can **vary** though.

5) In DNA there are **four** possible bases — adenine (**A**), thymine (**T**), cytosine (**C**) and guanine (**G**). In RNA, uracil (**U**) replaces thymine.

6) The mononucleotides are joined through **condensation reactions** between the **phosphate** of one mononucleotide and the **sugar** group of another. As in all condensation reactions, **water** is a by-product (see p. 8).

7) **DNA** is made of **two polynucleotide strands**, RNA has just **one strand**.

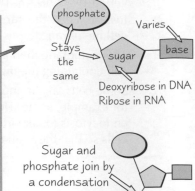

Sugar and phosphate join by a condensation reaction

Two DNA Strands Join Together to Form the DNA Double-Helix

1) **Two complementary** DNA strands join together by **hydrogen bonding** between the bases.

2) Each base can only join with one particular partner — this is called **complementary base pairing**.

3) **Adenine** always pairs with **thymine** (**A - T**) and **guanine** always pairs with **cytosine** (**G - C**).

4) The two DNA strands **wind up** to form the **DNA double-helix**.

> Complementary strands are DNA strands that can join together by complementary base pairing.

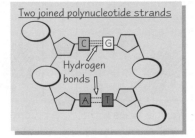

DNA can Copy Itself — Self-Replication

DNA copies itself before **cell division** (see p. 48) so that each new cell has the full amount of DNA.

1) The DNA helix **unzips** to form two single strands. Each original single strand acts as a **template** for a new strand.

2) Free-floating mononucleotides join to each original template strand by **complementary base pairing** — A with T, G with C.

3) The mononucleotides on the new strand are **joined together** by the enzyme **DNA polymerase**. Hydrogen bonds **form** between the bases on the original and new strand.

4) Each new DNA molecule contains **one strand** from the **original** DNA molecule and one **new strand**.

This type of copying is called **semi-conservative replication** because **half** of the new strands of DNA are from the **original** piece of DNA.

Structure of DNA and Replication

Meselson and Stahl Provided Evidence for Semi-conservative Replication

Before Meselson and Stahl's experiment people were unsure if DNA replication was **semi-conservative** or **conservative**. **Semi-conservative** replication would produce new DNA molecules containing **one original strand** and **one new strand**. If the method was **conservative**, the original DNA strands would **stay together** and the new DNA molecules would contain **two new strands**. Meselson and Stahl showed DNA replicated using the **semi-conservative method**. Their experiment used two **isotopes** of **nitrogen** (DNA contains nitrogen) — **heavy** nitrogen (^{15}N) and **light** nitrogen (^{14}N).

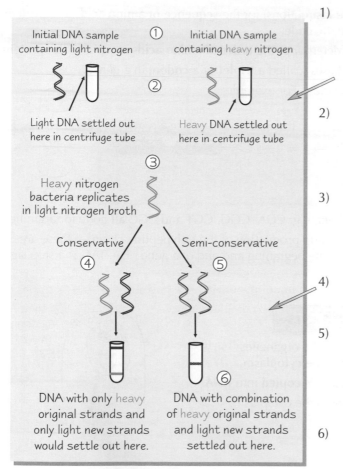

① Initial DNA sample containing light nitrogen / Initial DNA sample containing heavy nitrogen

② Light DNA settled out here in centrifuge tube / Heavy DNA settled out here in centrifuge tube

③ Heavy nitrogen bacteria replicates in light nitrogen broth

Conservative / Semi-conservative

④ / ⑤

⑥

DNA with only heavy original strands and only light new strands would settle out here. / DNA with combination of heavy original strands and light new strands settled out here.

1) Two samples of bacteria were grown — one in a nutrient broth containing **light** nitrogen, and one in a broth with **heavy** nitrogen. As the **bacteria reproduced**, they **took up nitrogen** from the broth to help make mononucleotides for new DNA. So the nitrogen gradually became part of the bacteria's DNA.

2) A **sample of DNA** was taken from each batch of bacteria, and spun in a **centrifuge**. The DNA from the **heavy** nitrogen bacteria settled **lower** down the **centrifuge tube** than the DNA from the **light** nitrogen bacteria — because it's **heavier**.

3) Then the bacteria grown in the **heavy** nitrogen broth were **taken out** and put in a broth containing only **light nitrogen**. The bacteria were left for **one round of DNA replication**, and then **another DNA sample** was taken out and spun in the centrifuge.

4) If replication was **conservative**, the original **heavy** DNA, which is still together, would settle at the bottom and the new **light** DNA would settle at the top.

5) If replication was **semi-conservative**, the new bacterial DNA molecules would contain **one strand** of the **old DNA** containing **heavy** nitrogen and **one strand** of **new DNA** containing **light** nitrogen. So the DNA would settle out **between** where the **light** nitrogen DNA settled out and where the **heavy** nitrogen DNA settled out.

6) The DNA settled out in the **middle**, showing that the DNA molecules contained a **mixture** of **heavy** and **light** nitrogen. The bacterial DNA had **replicated semi-conservatively** in the **light** nitrogen.

Practice Questions

Q1 What are the three main components of mononucleotides?

Q2 Which base pairs join together in a DNA molecule?

Q3 Describe three differences between DNA and RNA.

Exam Questions

Q1 Describe, using diagrams where appropriate, how mononucleotides are joined together in DNA and how two single polynucleotide strands of DNA are joined. [5 marks]

Q2 Describe the semi-conservative method of DNA replication. [7 marks]

Give me a D, give me an N, give me an A! What do you get? — very confused...

You need to know the basic structure of DNA and RNA and also how they join up to form polynucleotide strands. Then there's the semi-conservative method of DNA replication and Meselson and Stahl's lovely experiment to learn. The diagrams are handy for learning this kind of stuff — they're not just there to make the page look pretty. So get drawing.

The Genetic Code and Protein Synthesis

All that lovely DNA isn't just floating around in cells doing nothing. It's busy being used to make all the proteins that living organisms need to function. Confused? Not to worry, it's all covered below...

DNA Contains Genes Which are Instructions for Proteins

1) **Polypeptide chains** (**proteins**) are made from **amino acids**.

2) Different proteins have a **different number** and **order** of amino acids.

3) A gene is a **sequence of bases** that **codes** (contains the instructions) for the **sequence of amino acids** in a **protein**. The way that DNA codes for proteins is called the **genetic code**.

4) It's the **order** of **mononucleotide bases** in a gene that determines the **order of amino acids** in a particular **protein**.

5) Each amino acid is coded for by a sequence of **three bases** (called a **triplet** or a **codon**) in a gene.

6) Different sequences of bases code for different amino acids. For example:

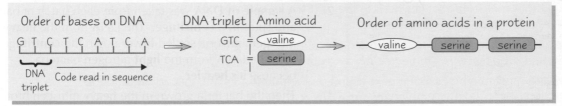

7) Some amino acids are coded for by **more than one** triplet, e.g. CGA, CGG, CGT and CGC **all** code for arginine.

8) Other triplets are used to tell the cell when to **start** and **stop** production of the polypeptide chain — these are called **start** and **stop** signals (**codons**). They're found at the beginning and end of a gene. E.g. TAG is a stop signal.

DNA is Copied into RNA for Protein Synthesis

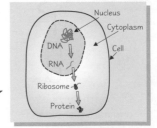

1) DNA molecules are found in the **nucleus** of the cell, but the organelles for protein synthesis (**ribosomes**, see p. 44) are found in the **cytoplasm**.

2) DNA is too large to move out of the nucleus, so a section is **copied** into **RNA**.

3) The RNA **leaves** the nucleus and joins with a **ribosome** in the cytoplasm, where it can be used to synthesise a **protein**.

First Stage of Protein Synthesis — Transcription

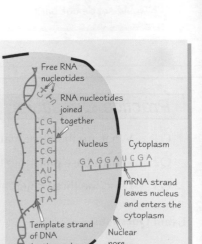

During transcription an **RNA copy** of a gene is made in the **nucleus**:

1) The **hydrogen bonds** between the two DNA strands in a **gene** break, **separating** the strands, and the DNA molecule **uncoils** at that point.

2) One of the strands is then used as a **template** to make an RNA copy, called **messenger RNA** (**mRNA**). The template strand is called the **antisense** strand.

   - **mRNA** is a **single polynucleotide** molecule.
   - **Complementary base pairing** means that the mRNA ends up being an exact **reverse copy** of the DNA template section (except the base **T** is replaced by **U** in **RNA**).

3) Free **RNA mononucleotides** line up alongside the template strand. Once the RNA mononucleotides have **paired up** with their complementary bases on the DNA strand they're joined together, forming an **mRNA** molecule.

4) The **mRNA** moves **out** of the **nucleus** through a nuclear pore, and attaches to a **ribosome** in the cytoplasm, where the next stage of protein synthesis takes place (see next page).

5) When enough mRNA has been produced, the hydrogen bonds between the uncoiled strands of DNA re-form, and the strands **coil back into a double helix**.

The Genetic Code and Protein Synthesis

Second Stage of Protein Synthesis — Translation

Translation occurs at the **ribosomes** in the **cytoplasm**. During **translation**, **amino acids** are stuck together to make a polypeptide chain (protein), following the order of bases on the mRNA.

1) The **mRNA** attaches itself to a **ribosome** and **transfer RNA** (**tRNA**) molecules carry **amino acids** to the ribosome.

- **tRNA** is a folded molecule made of a **single polynucleotide strand**.
- Each tRNA molecule has a **binding site** at one end, where a specific **amino acid** attaches.
- Each tRNA molecule also has a specific sequence of **three bases** at one end of it.

2) A tRNA molecule, with **complementary bases** to the **first triplet of bases** (codon) on the mRNA, attaches itself to the mRNA by **complementary base pairing**.

3) A second tRNA molecule attaches itself to the **next triplet of bases** on the mRNA in the **same way**.

The three bases on the tRNA molecule are called the anticodon.

4) The two amino acids attached to the tRNA molecules are **joined together** by a **peptide bond**. The first tRNA molecule **moves away**, leaving its amino acid behind.

5) A third tRNA molecule binds to the **next triplet** on the mRNA. Its amino acid **binds** to the first two and the second tRNA molecule **moves away**.

6) This process continues, producing a chain of linked amino acids (a **polypeptide chain**), until there's a **stop signal** on the mRNA molecule.

7) The polypeptide chain (protein) moves away from the ribosome and translation is complete.

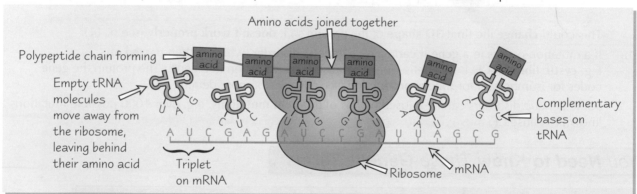

Amino acids joined together

Polypeptide chain forming

Empty tRNA molecules move away from the ribosome, leaving behind their amino acid

Triplet on mRNA

Complementary bases on tRNA

Ribosome

mRNA

Practice Questions

Q1 What is a gene?

Q2 Where does transcription take place?

Q3 Where does translation take place?

Exam questions

Amino acid	DNA triplet
Proline	CCG
Leucine	CTT CTC
Glycine	GGA
Threonine	ACC ACA
Start signal	ATG
Stop signal	TGA

Q1 a) Write the mRNA sequence that's complementary to the DNA sequence CTCACCCCGTGA. [2 marks]
    b) Use the table above to write the protein sequence coded for by the DNA sequence given in part a). [2 marks]
    c) Is the DNA sequence from a) found at the beginning or the end of a gene? Give a reason for your answer. [2 marks]

Q2 Describe the process of protein synthesis. [10 marks]

mRNA joins to tRNA at a ribosome — I need a translation please...

When you first go through protein synthesis it might make no sense, but I promise its bark is worse than its bite. All those strange words disguise what's really quite a straightforward process. Transcription — an mRNA copy of a section of DNA (a gene) is made. Translation — the mRNA copy and amino acids carried by tRNAs are used to make proteins.

Genes and Inheritance

This section is all about genetic disorders — inherited disorders caused by abnormal genes or chromosomes.
But first you need to understand how these disorders arise and learn a load of genetic terms — will the fun ever stop...

Some **Genetic Disorders** are **Caused** by **Mutations**

1)   Mutations are **changes** to the **base sequence** of DNA (see page 34).

2)   They can be caused by **errors** during **DNA replication**.

3)   The **type** of errors that can occur include:

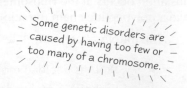
Some genetic disorders are caused by having too few or too many of a chromosome.

- **Substitution** — one base is substituted with another, e.g. AT**G**CCT becomes AT**T**CCT (G is **swapped** for T).
- **Deletion** — one base is deleted, e.g. AT**G**CCT becomes ATCCT (G is **deleted**).
- **Insertion** — an extra base is added, e.g. ATGCCT becomes ATG**A**CCT (an extra A is **added**).
- **Duplication** — one or more bases are repeated, e.g. ATG**CC**T becomes ATG**CCCC**T (two Cs are **duplicated**).
- **Inversion** — a sequence of bases is reversed, e.g. ATG**CCT** becomes ATG**TCC** (CCT is **reversed**).

4)   The **order** of **DNA bases** in a gene determines the **order of amino acids** in a particular **protein**. If a mutation occurs in a gene, the **primary structure** (the sequence of amino acids) of the protein it codes for could be **altered**:

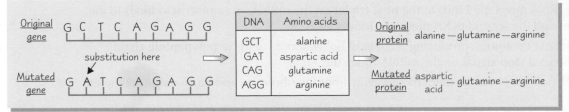

DNA	Amino acids
GCT	alanine
GAT	aspartic acid
CAG	glutamine
AGG	arginine

Original gene: G C T C A G A G G

substitution here

Mutated gene: G A T C A G A G G

Original protein: alanine — glutamine — arginine

Mutated protein: aspartic acid — glutamine — arginine

This could **change** the final **3D shape** of the protein so it **doesn't work properly** (see p. 11).

5)   If a mutation occurs in a **gene** it can cause a **genetic disorder**, which is then **passed on**. E.g. **cystic fibrosis (CF)** is a genetic disorder caused by a mutation in a gene. The protein the gene codes for is important for **mucus production** (see page 40 for more details).

6)   Some genetic disorders can be caused by lots of **different mutations**, e.g. over 1000 possible mutations are known to cause CF.

You **Need to Know** These **Genetic Terms**

TERM	DESCRIPTION
Gene	A sequence of bases on a DNA molecule that codes for a protein, which results in a characteristic, e.g. the gene for eye colour.
Allele	A different version of a gene. Most plants and animals, including humans, have two copies of each gene, one from each parent. The two copies can be the same or they can be different. Different versions (alleles) have slightly different base sequences, which code for different versions of the same characteristic, e.g. brown eyes and blue eyes. They're represented using letters, e.g. the allele for brown eyes (B) and the allele for blue eyes (b).
Genotype	The alleles a person has, e.g. BB, Bb or bb for eye colour.
Phenotype	The characteristics the alleles produce, e.g. brown eyes.
Dominant	An allele whose characteristic appears in the phenotype even when there's only one copy, e.g. the allele for brown eyes (B) is dominant — if a person's genotype is Bb or BB, they'll have brown eyes. Dominant alleles are shown by a capital letter.
Recessive	An allele whose characteristic only appears in the phenotype if two copies are present, e.g. the allele for blue eyes (b) is recessive — if a person's genotype is bb, they'll have blue eyes. Recessive alleles are shown by a lower case letter
Homozygote	An organism that carries two copies of the same allele, e.g. BB or bb.
Heterozygote	An organism that carries two different alleles, e.g. Bb.
Carrier	If a recessive allele can cause disease, a carrier is someone who has one dominant and one recessive allele (heterozygous). They won't have the disease but they carry a copy of the allele for the disease.

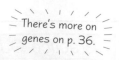
There's more on genes on p. 36.

Unfortunately, liking leotards and '80s legwarmers is a dominant characteristic.

Genes and Inheritance

Genetic Diagrams show the Possible Alleles of Offspring

Monohybrid inheritance is the inheritance of a **single characteristic** controlled by **different** alleles. **Genetic diagrams** can be used to predict the **genotypes** and **phenotypes** of the **offspring** produced if two parents are **crossed** (bred). You need to be able to **interpret** genetic diagrams for characteristics like garden pea plant seed morphology and height.

Seed Morphology

1) The **shape** of garden pea seeds is controlled by a **single** gene with **two alleles**.
2) The allele for **smooth** seeds (**S**) is **dominant** over the allele for **wrinkled** seeds (**s**).
3) The diagram below shows the predicted genotypes and phenotypes of the offspring if a **homozygous** pea plant with smooth seeds (**SS**) is crossed with a **heterozygous** pea plant with smooth seeds (**Ss**).

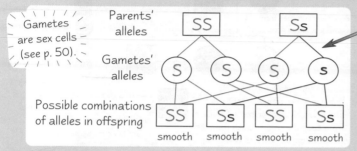

Gametes are sex cells (see p. 50).

The lines show all the possible ways the parents' alleles could combine.

Predicted genotypes and phenotypes:
- 2 in 4 (**50%**) **chance** of offspring having the **genotype SS**.
- 2 in 4 (**50%**) chance of offspring having the **genotype Ss**.
- **100%** chance of offspring having **smooth** seeds.

Plant Height

1) The **height** of garden pea plants is also controlled by a **single** gene with **two alleles**.
2) The allele for **tall** plants (**T**) is **dominant** over the allele for **dwarf** plants (**t**).
3) The diagram below shows the predicted genotypes and phenotypes of the offspring if **two heterozygous** pea plants (**Tt**) are crossed:

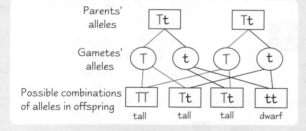

Predicted genotypes and phenotypes:
- 2 in 4 (**50%**) **chance** of offspring having the **genotype Tt** (phenotype = tall).
- 1 in 4 (**25%**) chance of offspring having the **genotype TT** (phenotype = tall).
- 1 in 4 (**25%**) chance of offspring having the **genotype tt** (phenotype = dwarf).

So there's a **75%** (3 in 4) chance of offspring being **tall**.

Practice Questions

Q1 What are mutations?

Q2 Explain the difference between a dominant and a recessive allele.

Q3 What is monohybrid inheritance?

Exam Question

Q1 A garden pea plant is heterozygous for seed colour. The allele for yellow colour (Y) is dominant over the allele for green colour (y).

a) Give the genotype and phenotype of the heterozygous plant. [2 marks]

b) Complete the genetic diagram above to show the possible genotypes of the offspring produced if the heterozygous plant is crossed with a homozygous plant with green seeds. [3 marks]

c) Give the predicted ratio of green seeds to yellow seeds in the offspring from the genetic cross in part b). [1 mark]

What do you get if you cross a one-legged donkey with a one-eyed donkey?*

There's quite a lot to get to grips with on these two pages — that list of genetic terms just goes on and on and on. You won't get very far in this section without learning them first though, so just grin and bear it. Oh... and learn it of course.

* A winky wonky donkey.

Inheritance of Genetic Disorders

Seeing as you enjoyed those genetic diagrams so much, here's another page of them — only this time they're ever so slightly different...

Genetic Pedigree Diagrams Show How Traits Run in Families

Genetic pedigree diagrams show an **inherited trait** (characteristic) in a group of **related individuals**. You need to be able to **interpret** genetic pedigree diagrams for the **genetic disorders** cystic fibrosis, albinism and thalassaemia. Here are some examples of pedigree diagrams for these genetic disorders:

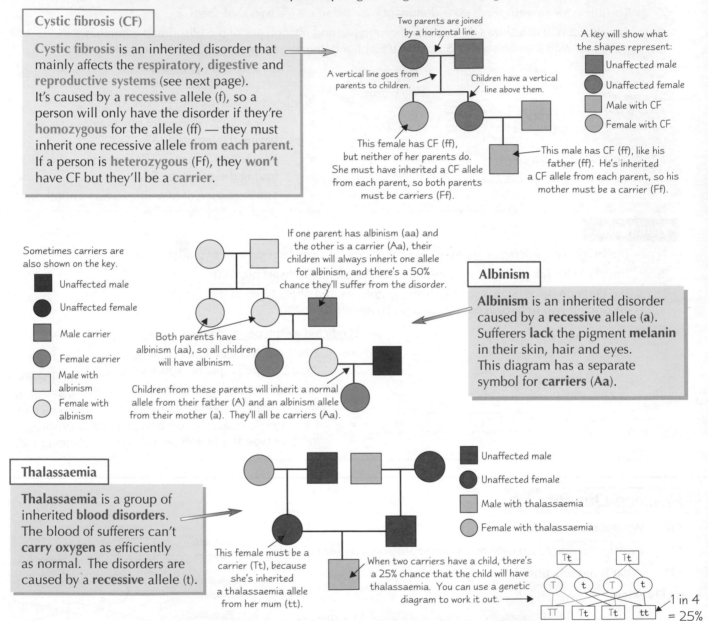

Cystic fibrosis (CF)

Cystic fibrosis is an inherited disorder that mainly affects the **respiratory, digestive** and **reproductive systems** (see next page). It's caused by a **recessive** allele (f), so a person will only have the disorder if they're **homozygous** for the allele (ff) — they must inherit one recessive allele **from each parent**. If a person is **heterozygous** (Ff), they **won't** have CF but they'll be a **carrier**.

Two parents are joined by a horizontal line.

A vertical line goes from parents to children.

Children have a vertical line above them.

A key will show what the shapes represent:
- Unaffected male
- Unaffected female
- Male with CF
- Female with CF

This female has CF (ff), but neither of her parents do. She must have inherited a CF allele from each parent, so both parents must be carriers (Ff).

This male has CF (ff), like his father (ff). He's inherited a CF allele from each parent, so his mother must be a carrier (Ff).

Sometimes carriers are also shown on the key.
- Unaffected male
- Unaffected female
- Male carrier
- Female carrier
- Male with albinism
- Female with albinism

If one parent has albinism (aa) and the other is a carrier (Aa), their children will always inherit one allele for albinism, and there's a 50% chance they'll suffer from the disorder.

Both parents have albinism (aa), so all children will have albinism.

Children from these parents will inherit a normal allele from their father (A) and an albinism allele from their mother (a). They'll all be carriers (Aa).

Albinism

Albinism is an inherited disorder caused by a **recessive** allele (**a**). Sufferers **lack** the pigment **melanin** in their skin, hair and eyes. This diagram has a separate symbol for **carriers** (**Aa**).

Thalassaemia

Thalassaemia is a group of inherited **blood disorders**. The blood of sufferers can't **carry oxygen** as efficiently as normal. The disorders are caused by a **recessive** allele (t).

This female must be a carrier (Tt), because she's inherited a thalassaemia allele from her mum (tt).

When two carriers have a child, there's a 25% chance that the child will have thalassaemia. You can use a genetic diagram to work it out.

- Unaffected male
- Unaffected female
- Male with thalassaemia
- Female with thalassaemia

1 in 4 = 25%

Cystic Fibrosis Causes the Production of Thick Sticky Mucus

1) Cystic fibrosis is caused by a **mutation** in the **gene** that codes for the **CFTR** protein (**C**ystic **F**ibrosis **T**ransmembrane **C**onductance **R**egulator).

2) CFTR is a **carrier protein** (see p. 32). It transports **chloride ions** out of cells and into **mucus** — this causes water to move **into** the mucus by **osmosis**, which makes mucus **watery**.

3) **Mutant** CFTR protein is much **less efficient** at transporting chloride ions **out** of the cell, so **less water moves out** **by osmosis**. This makes the mucus of people with CF abnormally **thick** and **sticky**.

4) This thick and sticky mucus causes **problems** in the **respiratory, digestive** and **reproductive systems**.

See pages 31-32 for more on osmosis and carrier proteins.

Inheritance of Genetic Disorders

Cystic Fibrosis Affects the **Respiratory System**...

Everybody has **mucus** in their respiratory system — it helps **prevent lung infections** by trapping **microorganisms**. The mucus (including the microorganisms) is transported towards the throat by **cilia** (small **hair-like** structures that beat to move mucus along). In people suffering from CF the mucus is abnormally **thick** and **sticky**, which causes some problems:

1) The cilia are **unable** to **move** the mucus towards the throat because it's so thick and sticky.

2) This means the **mucus builds up** in the **airways**.

3) Some airways can become completely **blocked** by the mucus — **gas exchange** can't take place in the area **below the blockage**.

See page 30 for more on gas exchange in the lungs.

4) This means that the **surface area** available for gas exchange is **reduced**, causing breathing difficulties.

5) Sufferers are also more prone to **lung infections** as mucus containing microorganisms can't be removed.

...the **Digestive System**...

Everyone also has mucus in their digestive system. The abnormally thick mucus produced by people suffering from CF can also cause **digestive problems** because:

1) The **tube** that connects the **pancreas** to the **small intestine** can become **blocked** with mucus — preventing **digestive enzymes** produced by the pancreas from **reaching** the small intestine. This reduces the sufferers ability to **digest food** and so **fewer nutrients** can be absorbed.

2) The mucus can cause **cysts** (**growths**) to form in the **pancreas**. These **inhibit** the **production** of **enzymes**, which also reduces the ability to digest food and absorb nutrients.

3) The mucus **lining** the **small intestine** is abnormally thick — this inhibits the **absorption** of nutrients.

...and the **Reproductive System**

Mucus is also secreted by the reproductive system — it helps to **prevent infections** and **transport sex cells** (sperm or eggs). The thick and sticky mucus of CF sufferers causes problems here because:

1) In men, the **tubes** connecting the **testicles** (where sperm are produced) to the **penis** are **absent** in some sufferers and can become **blocked** by the thick mucus in others. This means that any **sperm** produced **can't reach the penis**.

2) In women, thickened **cervical mucus** can **prevent** the sperm from **reaching the egg**. The sperm has to travel through this mucus to reach the egg — thick mucus reduces the **motility** of the sperm, reducing its chances of **making it** to the egg.

Jokes about genetic disorders aren't really PC — so here's a picture of a bear in a German police car and a chap sporting a silly hat.

Practice Questions

Q1 What is a genetic pedigree diagram?

Q2 Why do people suffering from cystic fibrosis have abnormally thick and sticky mucus?

Exam Question

Q1 The genetic pedigree diagram above shows the inheritance of cystic fibrosis (CF) in one family.

a) Name one female who is homozygous for the CF allele and one individual who is a carrier. [2 marks]

b) If James and Martha have another child, what is the chance it will have CF? Show your working. [3 marks]

c) Describe and explain the effect of CF on the digestive system. [8 marks]

Pedigree Diagram — because your dog's worth it...

Pedigree diagrams aren't as scary as they look, just work through them slowly. And remember — with recessive disorders affected individuals are always homozygous, so any children they have will always have at least one recessive allele.

Genetic Screening and Gene Therapy

Most genetic disorders can only be treated, not cured, so it's important to be able to screen for these conditions.

There are **Three Main Uses** of **Genetic Screening**

Genetic screening involves analysing **DNA** to see if it contains **alleles** for genetic disorders. The **three** main uses are:

(1) *Identification of* **Carriers**

1) **Carrier testing** is offered to individuals with a **family history** of genetic disorders.

2) It shows whether people **without** a disorder **carry an allele** that can cause a disorder (e.g. CF).

3) Couples can be tested **before having children** to determine the **chances** of any **future** children having the disorder, e.g. if both parents are **carriers** there's a **25%** chance their child will have the disorder.

4) Carrier testing allows people to make **informed decisions** about things like **whether to have children** and whether to carry out **prenatal testing** if the woman is pregnant (see below).

5) Carrier testing raises **social** and **ethical issues**:

- Finding out you're a carrier may cause **emotional stress** or affect your ability to **find a partner**.
- The tests **aren't** always **100% accurate** — they could give a **false result**. This means decisions could be based on **incorrect information**.
- Other genetic **abnormalities** may be found, which could cause **further stress**.
- There are concerns that the **results** of genetic tests could be used by **employers** or **life insurance companies** — resulting in **genetic discrimination**.

(2) *Preimplantation Genetic Diagnosis (PGD)*

1) **PGD** is carried out on **embryos** produced by *in vitro* fertilisation **(IVF)**.

2) It involves **screening** embryos for genetic disorders **before** they're implanted into the woman.

3) The **advantages** of PGD are that it **reduces** the chance of having a baby with a genetic disorder — only embryos **without** the genetic disorders tested for will be implanted. Also, because it's performed **before implantation**, it avoids the issue of **abortion** that could be raised by **prenatal testing** (see below).

4) PGD also raises **social** and **ethical issues**:

- It can be used to find out **other characteristics** (e.g. **gender, eye colour**) — leading to concerns that **in the future**, embryos may be selected for other characteristics (**designer babies**).
- **False results** could provide **incorrect information**.

Selecting for other characteristics is illegal in the UK.

(3) *Prenatal Testing*

1) Prenatal tests involve screening **unborn babies** (fetuses) for genetic disorders.

2) They're offered to pregnant women with a **family history** of genetic disease.

3) There are **two** types of test —

Amniocentesis	**Chorionic villus sampling (CVS)**
This is carried out at **15-16 weeks** of pregnancy. A sample of **amniotic fluid** (the fluid that surrounds the fetus) is obtained using a very fine **needle**. This fluid contains fetal **cells**. The cells contain **DNA**, which can be **analysed**.	This is carried out at **8-12 weeks** of pregnancy. A sample of **cells** is taken from the chorionic villi (part of the fetus that connects it to its mother) using a fine **needle** or a **catheter** (a thin flexible tube). The cells contain fetal **DNA**, which can be **analysed**.

4) Prenatal testing allows parents to make **informed decisions**. If the test is positive, the parents may decide to **have the child** or to have an **abortion**. The results can also help parents to **prepare for the future care** of the child — any **medical treatment** available could be started as soon as the child is born.

5) As with the other forms of testing, prenatal testing raises **social** and **ethical issues**:

- Prenatal tests slightly **increase** the risk of **miscarriage** (by around 1%).
- **False results** could provide **incorrect information**.
- Some people consider it **unethical** to **abort** a fetus because it has a genetic disorder.

Genetic Screening and Gene Therapy

Gene Therapy Could be Used to Cure Genetic Disorders

1) Gene therapy involves **altering** the **alleles** inside cells to cure **genetic disorders**.

2) How you do this depends on whether the genetic disorder is caused by a **dominant allele** or two **recessive alleles**:

Gene therapy is a new method, which isn't being used to treat people yet (some gene therapy treatments are undergoing clinical trials though).

- If it's caused by two **recessive** alleles you can **add** a working **dominant allele** to make up for them.
- If it's caused by a **dominant** allele you can 'silence' the **dominant allele** (e.g. by sticking a bit of DNA in the middle of the allele so it doesn't work any more).

3) Alleles are inserted into cells using **vectors** (**vehicles** that **carry** the alleles).

4) Different **vectors** can be used, e.g. altered **viruses** that can carry human DNA, **plasmids** (rings of bacterial DNA that can also carry human DNA) or **liposomes** (spheres made of lipid).

5) There are **two types** of gene therapy:

- **Somatic therapy** — this involves changing the alleles in **body cells**, particularly the cells that are **most affected** by the disorder. For example, CF is very **damaging** to the **respiratory system**, so somatic therapy for CF **targets** the epithelial cells lining the lungs. Somatic therapy doesn't affect the individual's **sex cells** (sperm or eggs) though, so any **offspring** could still **inherit** the disease.
- **Germ line therapy** — this involves changing the alleles in the **sex cells**. This means that **every cell** of **any offspring** produced from these cells will be **affected** by the gene therapy and they **won't suffer from the disease**. Germ line therapy in humans is currently illegal though.

Practice Questions

Q1 What is genetic screening?

Q2 Give the two uses of genetic screening other than prenatal testing.

Q3 Describe one ethical issue raised by prenatal testing.

Q4 What does gene therapy involve?

Q5 What is somatic gene therapy?

Q6 What is germ line gene therapy?

Exam Question

Q1 Duchenne muscular dystrophy is a genetic disorder caused by a recessive allele. It's caused by a mutated gene, which normally codes for a protein needed for healthy muscle tissue.

a) Explain why an individual with a family history of Duchenne muscular dystrophy may be offered carrier testing. [2 marks]

b) Preimplantation genetic diagnosis is available for Duchenne muscular dystrophy.

    i) Explain what preimplantation genetic diagnosis is. [1 mark]

    ii) Describe one benefit of preimplantation genetic diagnosis. [1 mark]

    iii) Describe two social or ethical issues raised by preimplantation genetic diagnosis. [2 marks]

c) Explain how somatic gene therapy could be used to treat Duchenne muscular dystrophy. [2 marks]

Gene therapy — counselling for Levis...

There's lots to learn when it comes to genetic screening and gene therapy. With genetic screening, you need to understand the three main uses, the advantages of each, and all the possible ethical issues. As with any ethics question in the exam, don't forget to cover both the advantages and the issues surrounding it (whatever your personal opinion).

Cells and Organelles

There's a vast amount of joy in store for you in this section — it's all about cells. The different types, all the bits and pieces inside of them, how they're organised, how they grow and divide... Sounds like endless amounts of fun.

Cells can be **Eukaryotic** or **Prokaryotic**

1) Eukaryotic cells are **complex** and include all **animal** and **plant cells**.

2) Prokaryotic cells are **smaller** and **simpler** (see next page).

The diagram on the right shows the **structure** of a typical **eukaryotic cell** (this one's an animal cell), including the **organelles** that are found inside. Organelles are **parts of cells** — each one has a **specific function**.

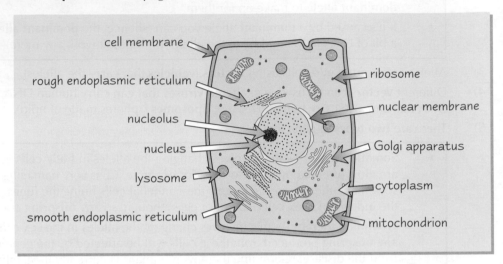

You need to *Know* the **Structure** and **Function** of *All These Organelles*

This table contains all the organelles found in **eukaryotic cells** that you need to know about. Most of them are surrounded by **membranes**, which sometimes causes confusion — don't make the mistake of thinking that a diagram of an organelle is a diagram of a **whole cell**. They're not cells — they're **parts of** cells, see.

ORGANELLE	DIAGRAM	DESCRIPTION	FUNCTION
Nucleus	nuclear envelope / nucleolus / nuclear pore / chromatin	A large organelle surrounded by a **nuclear envelope** (double membrane), which contains many **pores**. The nucleus contains **chromatin** and often a structure called the **nucleolus**.	**Chromatin** is made from proteins and DNA. The pores allow substances (e.g. RNA) to move between the nucleus and the cytoplasm. The **nucleolus** makes **ribosomes** (see below).
Lysosome		A **round organelle** surrounded by a **membrane**, with no clear internal structure.	Contains **digestive enzymes**. These are kept separate from the cytoplasm by the surrounding membrane, but can be used to **digest invading cells** or to **break down** worn out components of the cell.
Vesicle	cell's plasma membrane / vesicle	A small **fluid-filled sac** in the cytoplasm, surrounded by a membrane.	**Transports substances** in and out of the cell (via the cell membrane) and between organelles. Some are formed by the Golgi apparatus or the endoplasmic reticulum, while others are formed at the cell surface.
Ribosome	small subunit / large subunit	A **very small organelle** that **floats free** in the cytoplasm or is **attached** to the **rough endoplasmic reticulum**.	The **site** where **proteins** are **made**.

Cells and Organelles

ORGANELLE	DIAGRAM	DESCRIPTION	FUNCTION
Endoplasmic Reticulum (ER)	a) sER b) rER ribosome fluid	There are two types of endoplasmic reticulum: the **smooth ER** (diagram **a**) is a system of membranes enclosing a fluid-filled space. The **rough ER** (diagram **b**) is similar, but is **covered in ribosomes**.	The **smooth ER synthesises** and **processes lipids**. The **rough ER folds** and **processes proteins** that have been made at the ribosomes.
Golgi Apparatus	vesicle	A group of fluid-filled **flattened sacs**. Vesicles are often seen at the edges of the sacs.	It **processes** and **packages** new lipids and proteins. It also **makes lysosomes**.
Centriole		**Hollow cylinders**, containing a ring of microtubules (tiny protein cylinders).	Involved with the **separation of chromosomes** during cell division (see p. 48).
Mitochondrion	outer membrane inner membrane crista matrix	They're usually oval-shaped. They have a **double membrane** — the inner one is folded to form structures called **cristae**. Inside is the **matrix**, which contains enzymes involved in respiration.	The **site of aerobic respiration**, where **ATP** is produced. They're found in large numbers in cells that are very **active** and require a lot of **energy**.

Prokaryotic Cells are Simpler than Eukaryotic Cells

Prokaryotic cells include **bacteria** and **blue-green algae**.
The diagram below shows the structure of a typical prokaryotic cell.

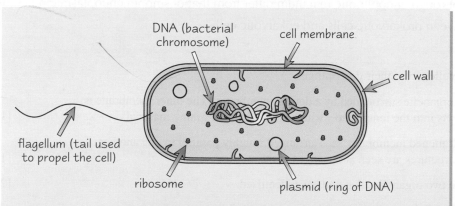

DNA (bacterial chromosome)
cell membrane
cell wall
flagellum (tail used to propel the cell)
ribosome
plasmid (ring of DNA)

Plasmids make a unique and elegant facial accessory.

You need to know the **differences** between eukaryotic cells and prokaryotic cells. So I've summarised them for you in this lovely table:

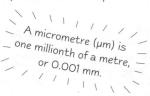

A micrometre (μm) is one millionth of a metre, or 0.001 mm.

EUKARYOTES	PROKARYOTES
Larger cells (2-200 μm diameter)	Extremely small cells (less than 2.0 μm diameter)
DNA is linear	DNA is circular
Nucleus present — DNA is inside nucleus	No nucleus — DNA free in cytoplasm
No cell wall (in animals), cellulose cell wall (in plants) or chitin cell wall (in fungi)	Cell wall made of a polysaccharide, but not cellulose or chitin
Many organelles, mitochondria present	Few organelles, no mitochondria
Large ribosomes	Smaller ribosomes
Example: Human liver cell	**Example:** *E. coli* bacterium

Cells and Organelles

Rough ER, Vesicles and Golgi Apparatus are Involved in Protein Transport

1) Proteins are made at the **ribosomes**.

2) The ribosomes on the **rough endoplasmic reticulum (rER)** make proteins that are **excreted** or attached to the **cell membrane**. The free ribosomes in the **cytoplasm** make proteins that **stay in the cytoplasm**.

3) New proteins produced at the rER are **folded** and **processed** (e.g. sugar chains are added) in the rER.

4) Then they're **transported** from the ER to the **Golgi apparatus** in **vesicles**.

5) At the Golgi apparatus, the proteins may undergo **further processing** (e.g. sugar chains are trimmed or more are added).

6) The proteins enter more **vesicles** to be transported around the cell. E.g. **extracellular enzymes** (like digestive enzymes) move to the cell surface and are **secreted**.

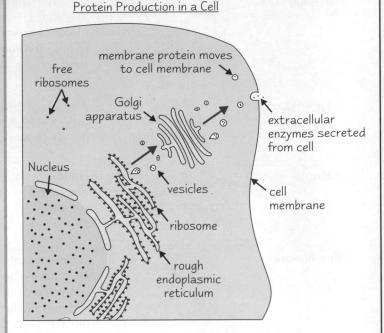

Protein Production in a Cell

Practice Questions

Q1 What is the function of the nucleolus?

Q2 Which organelle contains digestive enzymes?

Q3 How does the structure of rough endoplasmic reticulum differ from that of smooth endoplasmic reticulum?

Q4 Give two differences between prokaryotic cells and eukaryotic cells.

Exam questions

Q1 a) Identify these two organelles from their descriptions:

   i) An oval-shaped organelle surrounded by a double membrane. The inner membrane is folded and projects into the inner space, which is filled with a grainy material. [1 mark]

   ii) A collection of flattened membrane 'sacs' arranged roughly parallel to one another. Small, circular structures are seen at the edges of these 'sacs'. [1 mark]

   b) State the function of the two organelles that you have identified. [2 marks]

Q2 Some cells that secrete extracellular enzymes were immersed in a solution of radioactive amino acids. Every five seconds, some of the cells were removed and their organelles were separated and analysed. The radioactivity in the different organelles was measured for each five second interval.

   When answering the questions below, use organelles from this list — Golgi apparatus, ribosomes, rough endoplasmic reticulum, vesicles.

   a) In which of these organelles would you expect radioactivity to appear first? Explain your answer. [2 marks]

   b) After 5 minutes, the Golgi apparatus had become radioactive. Which other organelle(s) would be radioactive by this time? [3 marks]

That's enough talk of fluid-filled sacs for my liking. Scientists these days...

Organelle is a very pretty-sounding name for all those blobs. Actually, under a microscope some of them are really quite fetching — well I think so anyway, but then my mate finds sheep fetching, so there's no accounting for taste. Anyway, you need to know the names and functions of all the organelles and also what they look like.

Cell Organisation

Multicellular organisms (like us) are made up of lots of different cell types. To work together they need to be organised into groups, and those groups are grouped together, then the groups of groups are grouped... No wait... I'm confused...

Similar Cells are Organised into Tissues

Similar cells are grouped together into **tissues**. Here are two examples:

1) **Squamous epithelium tissue** is a **single layer** of **flat cells** lining a surface. Squamous epithelium tissue is found in many places, including the alveoli in the lungs.

2) **Xylem tissue** is a plant tissue with two jobs — it **transports water** around the plant, and it **supports** the plant. It contains **xylem vessel cells** and **parenchyma cells**.

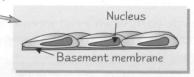

Nucleus
Basement membrane

Epithelium is a tissue that forms a covering or a lining.

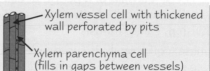

Xylem vessel cell with thickened wall perforated by pits
Xylem parenchyma cell (fills in gaps between vessels)

Tissues are Organised into Organs

An **organ** is a group of different tissues that **work together** to perform a particular function. Here are a couple of examples:

The leaf is an example of a plant organ. It's made up of the following **tissues**:

1) **Lower epidermis** — contains stomata (holes) to let air in and out for gas exchange.
2) **Spongy mesophyll** — full of spaces to let gases circulate.
3) **Palisade mesophyll** — most photosynthesis occurs here.
4) **Xylem** — carries water to the leaf.
5) **Phloem** — carries sugars away from the leaf.
6) **Upper epidermis** — covered in a waterproof waxy cuticle to reduce water loss.

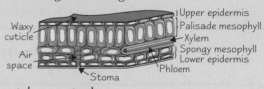

Waxy cuticle
Air space
Stoma
Upper epidermis
Palisade mesophyll
Xylem
Spongy mesophyll
Lower epidermis
Phloem

The lungs are an example of an animal organ. They're made up of the following **tissues**:

1) **Squamous epithelium tissue** — surrounds the alveoli (where gas exchange occurs).
2) **Fibrous connective tissue** — helps to force air back out of the lungs when exhaling.
3) **Blood vessels** — capillaries surround the alveoli.

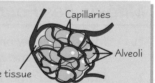

Capillaries
Alveoli
Connective tissue

Organs are Organised into Systems

Organs work together to form **organ systems** — each system has a **particular function**. Yup, you've guessed it, another example:

The **respiratory system** is made up of all the organs, tissues and cells involved in **breathing**.

The lungs, trachea, larynx, nose, mouth and diaphragm are all part of the respiratory system.

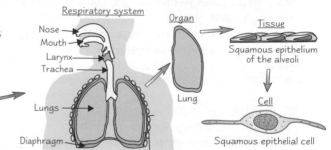

Respiratory system
Nose
Mouth
Larynx
Trachea
Lungs
Diaphragm
Organ
Lung
Tissue
Squamous epithelium of the alveoli
Cell
Squamous epithelial cell

Practice Question

Q1   Describe what is meant by the term tissue.

Exam Question

Q1   The liver is made of hepatocyte cells that form the main tissue, blood vessels to provide nutrients and oxygen, and connective tissue that holds the organ together. Discuss whether the liver is best described as a tissue or an organ.

[2 marks]

Soft and quilted — the best kind of tissues...

So, similar cells group together to form tissues. Then, because they love being so helpful, tissues work together in an organ to perform a particular function. OK, well maybe you need to know a bit more detail than that... but you get the idea.

The Cell Cycle and Mitosis

I don't like cell division. There, I've said it. It's unfair of me, because if it wasn't for cell division I'd still only be one cell big. It's all those diagrams that look like worms nailed to bits of string that put me off.

The **Cell Cycle** is the Process of **Cell Growth** and **Division**

The **cell cycle** is the process that all body cells from **multicellular organisms** use to **grow** and **divide**.

1) The cell cycle **starts** when a cell is produced by cell division and **ends** with the cell dividing to produce two identical cells.

2) The cell cycle consists of a period of **cell growth** and **DNA replication**, called **interphase**, and a period of **cell division**, called **mitosis**.

3) Interphase (cell growth) is sub-divided into three separate growth stages. These are called **G₁**, **S** and **G₂**.

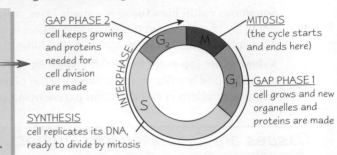

GAP PHASE 2
cell keeps growing and proteins needed for cell division are made

MITOSIS
(the cycle starts and ends here)

GAP PHASE 1
cell grows and new organelles and proteins are made

SYNTHESIS
cell replicates its DNA, ready to divide by mitosis

INTERPHASE

Mitosis is Used for *Growth*, *Repair* and *Asexual Reproduction*

1) Mitosis is needed for the **growth** of multicellular organisms (like us) and for **repairing damaged tissues**.

2) Some organisms (e.g. some **plants** and **fungi**) **reproduce asexually** (without sex) using mitosis. This means any new organisms produced are **genetically identical** to the original, parent organism.

Mitosis has *Four Division Stages*

1) Mitosis is really one **continuous process**, but it's described as a series of **division stages** — prophase, metaphase, anaphase and telophase.

2) **Interphase** comes **before** mitosis in the cell cycle — it's when cells grow and replicate their DNA ready for division.

<u>Interphase</u> — The cell carries out normal functions, but also prepares to divide. The cell's **DNA** is unravelled and **replicated**, to double its genetic content. The **organelles** are also **replicated** so it has spare ones, and its ATP content is increased (ATP provides the energy needed for cell division).

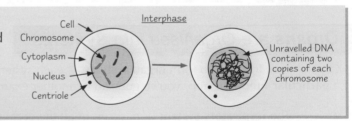

Interphase

Cell
Chromosome
Cytoplasm
Nucleus
Centriole

Unravelled DNA containing two copies of each chromosome

1) <u>Prophase</u> — The **chromosomes** **condense**, getting shorter and fatter. The **centrioles** (see p. 45) start moving to opposite ends of the cell, forming a network of protein fibres across it called the **spindle**. The **nuclear envelope** (the membrane around the nucleus) **breaks down** and chromosomes lie free in the cytoplasm.

Nuclear envelope starts to break down

Centrioles move to opposite ends of the cell

Centromere

As mitosis begins, the chromosomes are made of two strands joined in the middle by a <u>centromere</u>. The separate strands are called <u>chromatids</u>.

One chromatid — Centromere

Sister chromatids

There are two strands because each chromosome has already made an <u>identical copy</u> of itself during <u>interphase</u>. When mitosis is over, the chromatids end up as one-strand chromosomes in the new daughter cells.

2) <u>Metaphase</u> — The chromosomes (each with two chromatids) **line up** along the middle of the cell and become **attached** to the **spindle** by their **centromere**.

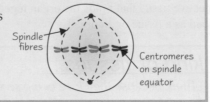

Spindle fibres

Centromeres on spindle equator

The Cell Cycle and Mitosis

3) <u>Anaphase</u> — The centromeres divide, **separating** each pair of sister **chromatids**. The spindles contract, pulling chromatids to opposite ends of the cell, centromere first.

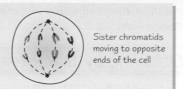

Sister chromatids moving to opposite ends of the cell

So long and thanks for all the organelles!

It's so hard letting go of my baby girls. It feels like a part of me has gone with them.

There, there love — it's all part of the cycle of life.

Mitosis can be a moving time.

4) <u>Telophase</u> — The chromatids reach the **opposite poles** on the spindle. They uncoil and become long and thin again. They're now called **chromosomes** again. A **nuclear envelope** forms around each group of chromosomes, so there are now **two nuclei**. The **cytoplasm divides** and there are now **two daughter cells** that are **genetically identical** to the original cell and to each other. Mitosis is finished and each daughter cell starts the **interphase** part of the cell cycle to get ready for the next round of mitosis.

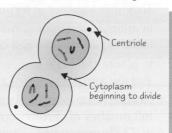

Centriole

Cytoplasm beginning to divide

Root Tips can be Stained to Observe Mitosis

You need to be able to describe how to **prepare** and **stain** a **root tip** in order to observe the **stages of mitosis**.

1) **Cut** the **tip** from a **growing root** (e.g. of a broad bean). Your root tip should be about **5 mm long**.

2) Place the root tip on a **watch glass** (a small, shallow bowl) and add a few drops of **hydrochloric acid**.

3) Add a few drops of **stain** so that the **chromosomes** become **darker** and so **easier to see** under a microscope. There are loads of different stains, all with crazy names — **toluidine blue**, **acetic orcein**, **Schiff's reagent**, **Feulgen's reagent**...

4) **Warm** the watch glass (but **don't boil** the liquid) by passing it slowly through a **Bunsen burner flame**.

5) Place the root tip on a **microscope slide** and use a **mounted needle** to **break it open** and spread the cells out thinly.

6) Add a few more drops of **stain** and then place a **cover slip** over it.

7) **Squash** the cover slip down gently.

8) **Warm** the slide again for a few seconds. This will **intensify** the stain.

9) Now you can look at all the stages of mitosis under a light microscope. Lovely.

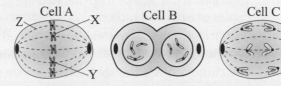

Root cells stained with Feulgen's reagent

Telophase
Prophase
Anaphase
Metaphase
Interphase

HERVE CONGE, ISM/SCIENCE PHOTO LIBRARY

Practice Questions

Q1 During what stage of the cell cycle does DNA replication occur?

Q2 Give three main uses of mitosis.

Q3 List in order the four stages of mitosis.

Exam Questions

Q1 The diagrams show cells at different stages of mitosis.

Cell A — Z, X, Y   Cell B   Cell C

a) For each of the cells A, B and C state the stage of mitosis, giving a reason for your answer. [6 marks]

b) Name the structures labelled X, Y and Z in cell A. [3 marks]

Q2 Briefly describe how to prepare a root tip to observe mitosis. [8 marks]

<u>Doctor, I'm getting short and fat — don't worry, it's just a phase...</u>

Quite a lot to learn on these pages — but it's all dead important stuff, so no slacking. Most cells undergo mitosis — it's how they multiply and how organisms like us grow and develop. Remember that chromosomes are in fact usually made up of two sister chromatids joined by a centromere. Nice to know family values are important to genetic material too.

Production of Gametes

Ahh, now on to some really exciting stuff — the production of gametes (sex cells to you and me) and sexual reproduction in plants and animals (oooh errr).

DNA is Passed to New Offspring by Gametes

1) **Gametes** are the male and female **sex cells** found in all organisms that reproduce **sexually**.

2) They join together at **fertilisation** to form a **zygote**, which divides and develops into a **new organism**.

3) In animals, the male gametes are **sperm** and the females gametes are **egg cells** (ova).

4) In plants, the male gametes are contained in **pollen grains** and the females gametes are contained in **ovules** (see p. 53).

5) Normal body cells of plants and animals contain the **full number** of chromosomes. Humans have **two sets** of **23 chromosomes** — one set from each parent — giving each body cell a total of **46 chromosomes**.

6) **Gametes** contain **half** the number of chromosomes as body cells — they only contain **one set** (23 in total for humans).

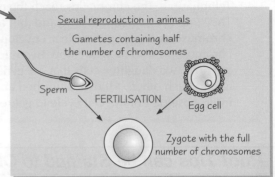

Sexual reproduction in animals

Gametes containing half the number of chromosomes

Sperm   FERTILISATION   Egg cell

Zygote with the full number of chromosomes

Mammalian Gametes are Specialised for Their Function

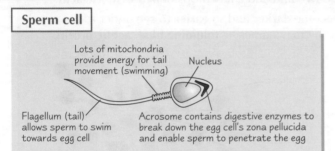

Sperm cell

Lots of mitochondria provide energy for tail movement (swimming)   Nucleus

Flagellum (tail) allows sperm to swim towards egg cell

Acrosome contains digestive enzymes to break down the egg cell's zona pellucida and enable sperm to penetrate the egg

Egg cell

Cell membrane

Follicle cells form protective coating

Zona pellucida — protective layer that sperm have to penetrate

Nucleus

Egg cells are much larger than sperm.

Cell Division by Meiosis Produces Gametes

1) **Meiosis** is a type of cell division that happens in the **reproductive organs** to produce **gametes**.

2) Cells that divide by meiosis have the **full number** of chromosomes to start with, but the cells that are formed from meiosis have **half the number**.

3) Without meiosis, you'd get **double** the number of chromosomes when the gametes **fused** at fertilisation. Not good.

You don't need to learn the stages of meiosis, just understand that it produces genetically different gametes.

Here's a brief overview of meiosis:

1) The DNA **replicates** so there are **two** identical copies of **each** chromosome, called **chromatids**.

2) The DNA condenses to form double-armed chromosomes, made from **two sister chromatids**.

3) The chromosomes arrange themselves into **homologous pairs** — pairs of **matching** chromosomes (one from each set of 23 — e.g. both number 1s).

4) **First division** — the homologous **pairs** are **separated**, **halving** the chromosome number.

5) **Second division** — the pairs of sister **chromatids** are separated.

6) **Four new cells** (gametes) that are **genetically different** from each other are produced.

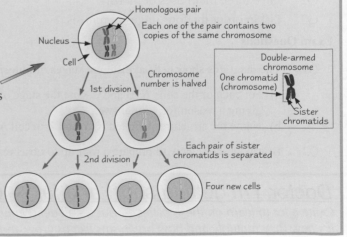

Homologous pair

Each one of the pair contains two copies of the same chromosome

Nucleus

Cell

1st divsion

Chromosome number is halved

2nd division

Each pair of sister chromatids is separated

Four new cells

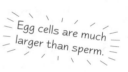

Double-armed chromosome

One chromatid (chromosome)

Sister chromatids

Production of Gametes

Meiosis Produces Cells that are Genetically Different

Genetic variation is the **differences** that exist between **individuals' genetic material**. The reason that meiosis is so important is that it **creates** genetic variation — it makes gametes that are genetically different. It does this in two ways:

① Crossing over of chromatids

1) Before the first division of meiosis, **homologous pairs** of chromosomes come together and **pair up**.

2) Two of the **chromatids** in each homologous pair **twist around** each other.

3) The twisted bits **break off** their original chromatid and **rejoin** onto the other chromatid, **recombining** their genetic material.

Chromatids of one chromosome   Crossing over occurs between chromatids   Chromatids now have a new combination of alleles

 Each homologous pair of chromosomes pairs up

Chromatids cross over

1st division

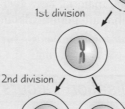

One chromosome from each homologous pair ends up in each cell

2nd division

Each cell has a different chromatid and therefore a different set of alleles, which increases genetic variation.

4) The chromatids still contain the **same genes** but they now have a **different combination** of alleles.

5) This means that each of the **four new cells** formed from meiosis contains chromatids with **different alleles**.

② Independent assortment of chromosomes

1) The four daughter cells formed from meiosis have completely **different combinations** of **chromosomes**.

2) All your cells have a **combination** of chromosomes from your parents, half from your mum (**maternal**) and half from your dad (**paternal**).

3) When the gametes are produced, different **combinations** of those maternal and paternal **chromosomes** go into each cell.

4) This is called **independent assortment** (separation) of the chromosomes.

Paternal   Maternal   OR

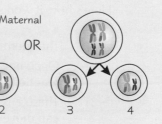

Possible new cells   1   2   3   4

Practice Questions

Q1   Name the male and female gametes of flowering plants.

Q2   What is the zona pellucida?

Q3   What name is given to the process that produces gametes?

Exam Questions

Q1   Describe how sperm are specialised for their function.   [3 marks]

Q2   a) Explain what crossing over is and how it leads to genetic variation.   [5 marks]

     b) Explain how independent assortment leads to genetic variation.   [2 marks]

Reproduction isn't as exciting as some people would have you believe...

This page is quite tricky, so use the diagrams to help you understand — they might look evil, but they really do help. The key thing to understand is that meiosis produces four genetically different daughter cells. And that the genetic variation in the daughter cells occurs because of two processes — crossing over and independent assortment.

Fertilisation

Right, now that you know how gametes are formed, you can get on to some fertilisation. I won't tell you any more because it's all explained on these pages. You have to read it though — don't just giggle at the rude diagram...

Fertilisation is When Male and Female Gametes Fuse

1) **Fertilisation** is the term used to describe the **exact moment** when the **nuclei** of the male and female gametes **fuse**.

2) Since each gamete contains **half** the full number of chromosomes, fertilisation creates a cell with the **full** number of chromosomes — this cell is called the **zygote**.

3) The zygote contains **two** sets of chromosomes — one set from the **male** parent and one from the **female** parent.

4) **Combining** genetic material from **two individuals** makes offspring that are **genetically unique**.

NB: you can't fertilise farmland with sperm.

In Mammals Fertilisation Occurs in the Oviduct

1) In mammals, **sperm** (see page 50) are deposited high up in the female **vagina** close to the entrance of the **cervix**.

2) Once there, they have to make their way up through the **cervix** and **uterus**, and into one of the **oviducts**. The diagram on the right shows the **human** female reproductive system.

3) Once the sperm are in the oviduct **fertilisation** may occur. Here's how it works:

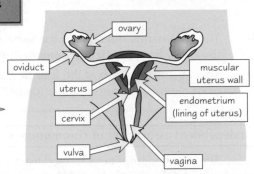

1) The sperm swim towards the **egg cell** in the oviduct.

2) Once **one** sperm makes contact with the **zona pellucida** of the egg cell (see page 50), the **acrosome reaction** occurs — this is where **digestive enzymes** are released from the acrosome of the sperm.

3) These enzymes **digest** the zona pellucida, so that the sperm can move through it to the cell membrane of the egg cell.

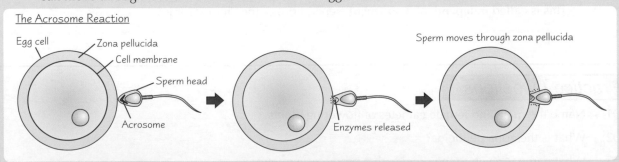

The Acrosome Reaction

Egg cell — Zona pellucida — Cell membrane — Sperm head — Acrosome — Enzymes released — Sperm moves through zona pellucida

4) The sperm head **fuses** with the **cell membrane** of the egg cell. This triggers the **cortical reaction** — the egg cell releases the contents of vesicles called **cortical granules** into the space between the cell membrane and the zona pellucida.

5) The chemicals from the cortical granules make the zona pellucida **thicken**, which makes it **impenetrable** to other sperm. This makes sure that **only one** sperm fertilises the egg cell.

6) Only the **sperm nucleus** enters the egg cell — its **tail** is **discarded.**

7) The nucleus of the sperm **fuses** with the nucleus of the egg cell — this is **fertilisation**.

A **zygote** is now formed, which has the full number of chromosomes. It immediately begins to divide by **mitosis** (see page 48) to develop into a fully formed organism.

Fertilisation

In Flowering Plants Fertilisation Occurs in the Embryo Sac

1) A pollen grain lands on the **stigma** of a flower. The grain **absorbs water** and **splits open**.

2) A **pollen tube** grows out of the pollen grain down the **style** (the rod-like section that supports the stigma). There are **three nuclei** in the pollen tube — one **tube nucleus** at the tube's **tip** and two **male gamete nuclei** behind it. The tube nucleus makes **enzymes** that **digest** surrounding cells, making a **way through** for the pollen tube.

3) When the tube reaches the **ovary**, it grows through the **micropyle** (a tiny hole in the ovule wall) and into the **embryo sac** within the **ovule**.

4) In the embryo sac, the tube nucleus **disintegrates** and the tip of the pollen tube **bursts**, releasing the two male nuclei.

5) One male nucleus fuses with the **egg nucleus** to make a **zygote**. This divides by mitosis to become the **embryo** of the seed.

6) The second male nucleus fuses with two other nuclei (called the **polar nuclei**) at the centre of the **embryo sac**. This produces a cell with a **large nucleus**, which divides to become a **food store** (called the **endosperm**) for the mature seed.

7) So a **double fertilisation** has taken place (**two** male nuclei have fused with female nuclei). This only happens in flowering plants.

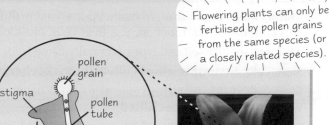

Flowering plants can only be fertilised by pollen grains from the same species (or a closely related species).

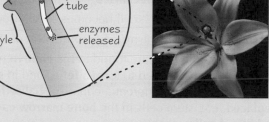

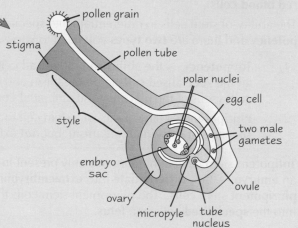

Practice Questions

Q1 What is fertilisation?

Q2 How many nuclei are found in a pollen tube?

Q3 What is the purpose of the endosperm?

Q4 What type of plants does double fertilisation occur in?

Exam Questions

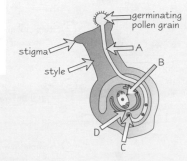

Q1 a) The diagram on the right shows the events leading to fertilisation in a flowering plant. Label parts A-D. [4 marks]

b) Explain why the pollen tube needs to secrete digestive enzymes. [2 marks]

Q2 Describe the process of fertilisation in mammals, starting with the acrosome reaction. [9 marks]

Polar nuclei — suitable for freezing...

You don't need to learn the diagram of the female reproductive system — it's just there to give words like 'oviduct' and 'uterus' some sort of meaning when you're trying to learn what goes where. See, never say that I don't try my very best to help you. Now help yourself and get this stuff learnt — then it'll be another section done and dusted.

Cell Differentiation

If I had to choose a favourite type of cell, I'd choose a stem cell and here's why...

Stem Cells Are Able to Differentiate into Specialised Cells

1) **Multicellular organisms** are made up from many **different cell types** that are **specialised** for their function, e.g. liver cells, muscle cells, white blood cells.

2) **All** these specialised cell types originally came from **stem cells**.

3) Stem cells are **unspecialised** cells that can develop into **any** type of cell.

4) Stem cells divide by **mitosis** (see page 48) to become **new** cells, which then become **specialised**.

5) The **process** by which a cell becomes specialised is called **differentiation**.

6) All multicellular organisms have some form of stem cell.

7) In **humans**, stem cells are found in the **embryo** (where they differentiate into **all** the cells needed to form a **fetus**) and in **some adult tissues** (where they differentiate into **specialised** cells that need to be **replaced**, e.g. stem cells in the **bone marrow** can differentiate into **red blood cells**).

8) The ability of stem cells to differentiate into specialised cells is called **potency** and there are **two types** you need to know about:

> 1) **Totipotency** — the ability to produce **all cell types**, including all the **specialised cells** in an organism and **extraembryonic cells** (cells of the placenta and umbilical cord).
>
> 2) **Pluripotency** — the ability of a stem cell to produce all the **specialised cells** in an organism (but **not** extraembryonic cells).

9) **Totipotent** stem cells in humans are only present in the **early life** of an **embryo** — they **differentiate** into **extraembryonic** cells and **pluripotent** stem cells. The pluripotent stem cells then **differentiate** into the **specialised** cells in a **fetus**.

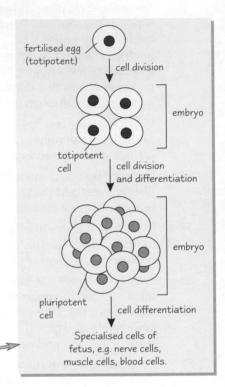

fertilised egg (totipotent)

cell division

embryo

totipotent cell

cell division and differentiation

embryo

pluripotent cell

cell differentiation

Specialised cells of fetus, e.g. nerve cells, muscle cells, blood cells.

Totipotency Can be Demonstrated by Plant Tissue Culture

1) **Plants** also have **stem cells** — they're found in areas where the plant is **growing**, e.g. in roots and shoots.

2) All stem cells in plants are **totipotent** — they can produce **all cell types** and can grow into a **whole new plant**.

3) Totipotency can be shown in plants using **tissue culture**, a method used to **grow** a **plant** from a **single cell**:

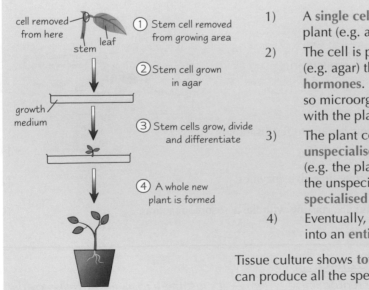

cell removed from here
leaf
stem
① Stem cell removed from growing area
② Stem cell grown in agar
growth medium
③ Stem cells grow, divide and differentiate
④ A whole new plant is formed

1) A **single cell** is taken from a **growing area** on a plant (e.g. a **root** or **shoot**).

2) The cell is placed in some **growth medium** (e.g. agar) that contains **nutrients** and **growth hormones**. The growth medium is **sterile**, so microorganisms can't grow and compete with the plant cells.

3) The plant cell will **grow** and **divide** into a **mass** of **unspecialised** cells. If the **conditions** are **suitable** (e.g. the plant cells are given the **right hormones**) the unspecialised cells will **differentiate** into **specialised** cells.

4) Eventually, the cells will grow and differentiate into an **entire plant**.

Tissue culture shows **totipotency** because a **single stem** cell can produce all the specialised cells to make a **whole plant**.

Cell Differentiation

Stem Cells Become Specialised Through Differential Gene Expression

Stem cells become **specialised** because different genes in their DNA become **active** (are turned on) — in other words they **express different genes** (use different genes to make different **proteins**):

1) **Stem cells** all contain the **same genes**, but not all of them are **expressed** because not all of them are **active**.

2) Under the **right conditions**, some **genes** are **activated** and other genes are **inactivated**.

3) **mRNA** is only **transcribed** from the **active genes**.

4) The mRNA from the active genes is then **translated** into **proteins**.

5) These proteins **modify** the cell — they determine the cell **structure** and **control cell processes** (including the activation of **more** genes, which produces more proteins).

6) **Changes** to the cell produced by these proteins cause the cell to become **specialised** (**differentiate**). These changes are **difficult** to **reverse**, so once a cell has differentiated it **stays** specialised.

Alfie had become specialised in the art of hide and seek...

There's more on transcription and translation on pages 36-37.

Example — Red Blood Cells

1) **Red blood cells** are produced from a type of **stem cell** in the **bone marrow**. They contain lots of **haemoglobin** and have **no nucleus** (to make room for more haemoglobin).

2) The stem cell produces a new cell in which the genes for **haemoglobin production** are **activated**. Other genes, such as those involved in **removing the nucleus**, are **activated** too. Many other genes are activated or inactivated, resulting in a specialised red blood cell.

Practice Questions

Q1 What are stem cells?

Q2 What is the process by which a stem cell becomes specialised called?

Q3 Name the method that can be used to demonstrate totipotency in plant cells?

Exam Questions

Q1 Explain what is meant by the terms totipotent stem cell and pluripotent stem cell. [5 marks]

Q2 Describe how differential gene expression results in the production of specialised cells. [6 marks]

And you thought differentiation was just boring maths stuff...

Stem cells are pretty amazing when you think about it — they can differentiate to become any cell in the whole body. Totipotent stem cells are the coolest cells though — they can divide and differentiate into a whole organism. Handy party trick that. Beats mine — fitting my whole fist in my mouth... shhheeee, it'shhhh a bitssshhhh hard to talkkkkk though...

Stem Cells in Medicine

These pages are about how stem cells can be used in medicine to replace damaged cells. It's got me thinking... perhaps I could grow another brain from some of my stem cells — then I'd be twice as clever... By jove, I think it'd work.

Stem Cells Could be Used to Treat Some Diseases

1) **Stem cells** can develop into **any** specialised cell type, so scientists think they could be used to **replace damaged tissues** in a **range** of **diseases**.

2) Some stem cell therapies **already exist**. For example, the treatment for **leukaemia** (a cancer of the bone marrow) kills all the **stem cells** in the bone marrow, so **bone marrow transplants** can be given to patients to **replace** them.

3) Scientists are **researching** the use of stem cells as a **treatment** for lots of conditions, including:
   - **Spinal cord injuries** — stem cells could be used to repair damaged **nerve tissue**.
   - **Heart disease** and **damage caused by heart attacks** — stem cells could be used to replace damaged heart tissue.

4) People who make **decisions** about the **use** of stem cells in medicine and research have to consider the **potential benefits** of stem cell therapies:
   - They could **save** many **lives** — e.g. many people waiting for organ transplants **die** before a **donor organ** becomes available. Stem cells could be used to **grow organs** for those people awaiting transplants.
   - They could **improve** the **quality of life** for many people — e.g. stem cells could be used to replace damaged cells in the eyes of people who are **blind**.

Human Stem Cells Can Come from Adult Tissue or Embryos

1) In order to **use stem cells** in medicine and research, scientists have to get them from somewhere.

2) There are **two** potential **sources** of human stem cells:

1 Adult stem cells

1) These are obtained from the **body tissues** of an **adult**. For example, adult stem cells are found in **bone marrow**.

2) They can be obtained in a relatively **simple operation** — with very **little risk** involved, but quite a lot of discomfort. The **donor** is anaesthetised, a **needle** is **inserted** into the centre of a **bone** (usually the hip) and a **small quantity** of bone marrow is **removed**.

3) Adult stem cells **aren't** as **flexible** as embryonic stem cells — they can only develop into a **limited** range of cells.

2 Embryonic stem cells

1) These are obtained from **early embryos**.

2) Embryos are created in a **laboratory** using *in vitro* fertilisation (IVF) — **egg cells** are **fertilised** by sperm **outside the womb**.

3) Once the embryos are approximately **4 to 5 days old, stem cells** are **removed** from them and the rest of the embryo is **destroyed**.

4) Embryonic stem cells can develop into **all types** of specialised cells.

3) Obtaining stem cells from **embryos** created by IVF raises **ethical issues** because the procedure results in the **destruction** of an embryo that's **viable** (could become a fetus if placed in a womb).

4) Many people believe that at the moment of **fertilisation** a **genetically unique individual** is formed that has the **right** to **life** — so they believe that it's **wrong** to **destroy** embryos.

5) Some people have **fewer objections** to stem cells being **obtained** from **unfertilised embryos** — embryos made from **egg cells** that **haven't** been fertilised by sperm. This is because the embryos **aren't viable** — they **can't survive** past a few days and **wouldn't** produce a fetus if placed in a womb.

6) Some people think that **scientists** should **only use** adult stem cells because their production **doesn't** destroy an embryo. But adult stem cells **can't** develop into all the specialised cell types that embryonic stem cells can.

7) The decision-makers in **society** have to take into account **everyone's views** when making decisions about **important scientific work** like stem cell research and its use in medicine.

Stem Cells in Medicine

Society Makes Decisions About the Use of Stem Cells in Medicine

1) Embryonic stem cells could be really **useful** in **medicine**, but **research** into their use raises many **ethical issues** (see previous page).

2) **Society** has to consider all the arguments **for** and **against** stem cell research before allowing it to go ahead.

3) To help society make these decisions, **regulatory authorities** have been established to consider the **benefits** and **ethical issues** surrounding embryonic stem cell research.

4) The work of regulatory authorities includes:

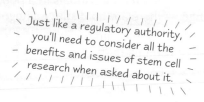
Just like a regulatory authority, you'll need to consider all the benefits and issues of stem cell research when asked about it.

1) Looking at proposals of **research** to decide if they should be **allowed** — this ensures that any research involving embryos is carried out for a **good reason**. This also makes sure research isn't unnecessarily **repeated** by different groups.

2) **Licensing** and **monitoring centres** involved in embryonic stem cell research — this ensures that only **fully trained staff** carry out the research. These staff will understand the **implications** of the research and **won't** waste precious resources, such as embryos. This also helps to **avoid unregulated research**.

3) Producing **guidelines** and **codes of practice** — this ensures all scientists are working in a **similar manner** (if scientists don't use similar methods their results can't be compared). It also ensures methods of **extraction** are **controlled**.

4) **Monitoring developments** in scientific research and advances — this ensures that any changes in the field are **regulated appropriately** and that all the **guidelines** are **up to date** with the latest in scientific understanding.

5) Providing **information** and **advice** to governments and professionals — this helps to **promote** the science involved in embryo research, and it helps **society** to **understand** what's involved and why it's important.

Practice Questions

Q1 Describe how stem cells could be used to treat a range of diseases.

Q2 Name two potential sources of human stem cells.

Q3 Describe the difference in flexibility between the two potential sources of human stem cells.

Exam Question

Q1 Stem cell research is permitted in the UK, but it is regulated by a number of authorities.

a) Describe one potential benefit of using stem cells in medicine. [1 mark]

b) Embryonic stem cells can be used for research.

  i) Explain how embryonic stem cells are obtained. [3 marks]

  ii) Suggest two reasons why some people are opposed to using stem cells from embryos. [2 marks]

Stem cells — I think they prove that we all evolved from plants...

Stem cells have the potential to cure or relieve the symptoms of some diseases, but as you've seen, there are some issues surrounding embryonic stem cells. Scientists are working towards producing stem cells that are as flexible as embryonic stem cells (i.e. can become any cell type) but that have come from other sources (e.g. the skin or bone marrow).

Variation

Ever wondered why no two people are exactly alike? No, well nor have I, actually, but it's time to start thinking about it. Variation is the differences that exist between individuals — it's partly due to genes and partly due to differences in the environment.

Variation in **Phenotype** can be **Continuous** or **Discontinuous**

> Phenotype is the characteristics displayed by an organism.

Continuous variation

This is when the individuals in a population vary **within a range** — there are **no distinct categories**. For example:

Height — you could be any height within a range.

Mass — you could be any mass within a range.

Skin colour — any shade from very dark to very pale.

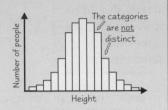

The categories are *not* distinct

Discontinuous variation

This is when there are two or more **distinct categories** — each individual falls into **only one** of these categories. For example:

Sex — male or female.

Blood group — you can be group A, group B, group AB or group O, but nothing else.

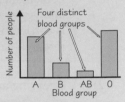

Four distinct blood groups

Variation in **Phenotype** is Influenced by **Variation in Genotype (Genes)**...

1) Individuals of the same species have **different genotypes** (different combinations of alleles).

2) This **variation in genotype** results in **variation** in **phenotype** — the **characteristics** displayed by an organism.
   For example, in humans there are six different combinations of blood group alleles, which can produce one of four different blood groups.

> There's more about alleles on page 38.

3) Some characteristics are controlled by only **one gene** — they're called **monogenic**. They tend to show **discontinuous variation**, e.g. blood group.

4) Most characteristics are controlled by a **number of genes** at **different loci** — they're said to be **polygenic**. They usually show **continuous variation**, e.g. height.

> **Different alleles** for the **same gene** are found in the **same position** on **chromosomes**. This position is called the **locus**.
>
>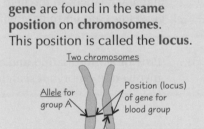

...and the **Environment**

1) Some characteristics are **only influenced** by **genotype**, e.g. blood group.

2) **Most** characteristics are influenced by **both** genotype and the environment, e.g. weight.

3) You need to learn what influences these four characteristics:

> 1) <u>Height</u> is **polygenic** and affected by **environmental factors**, especially **nutrition**. E.g. **tall parents** usually have **tall children**, but if the children are **undernourished** they **won't** grow to their **maximum height** (because **protein** is required for **growth**).

> 2) <u>Monoamine Oxidase A</u> (MAOA) is an **enzyme** that breaks down **monoamines** (a type of **chemical**) in **humans**. **Low levels** of MAOA have been linked to **mental health problems**. MAOA production is controlled by a **single gene** (it's **monogenic**), but taking **anti-depressants** or **smoking tobacco** can **reduce** the amount produced.

> 3) <u>Cancer</u> is the **uncontrolled division of cells** that leads to lumps of cells (**tumours**) forming. The **risk of developing** some cancers is affected by **genes**, but **environmental factors** such as **diet** can also **influence** the risk.

> 4) <u>Animal hair colour</u> is **polygenic**, but the environment also plays a part in **some** animals. E.g. some **arctic animals** have **dark hair** in **summer** but **white hair** in **winter**. **Environmental factors** like decreasing temperature **trigger** this change but it **couldn't** happen if the animal **didn't** have the **genes** for it.

Variation

It's Difficult to *Interpret* the *Relative Contributions* of *Genes* and *Environment*

1) Data on variation can be very tricky to **interpret** because some characteristics can be affected by **many different genes** (they're polygenic) and **many environmental factors**.

2) It's difficult to know **which factors** (genes or environment) are having the **greatest effect**.

3) This makes it **hard** to **draw conclusions** about the **causes of variation**.

Here's an example:

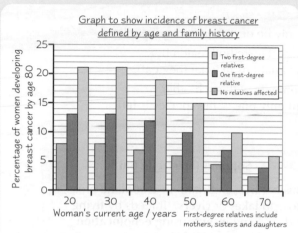

Graph to show incidence of breast cancer defined by age and family history

This graph shows how the **incidence** of **breast cancer** is affected by both **age** and **family history**. A woman is **more likely** to develop breast cancer if **members of her family** have had breast cancer, which suggests a **genetic link**.

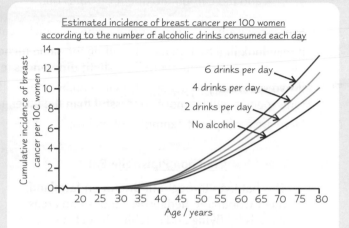

Estimated incidence of breast cancer per 100 women according to the number of alcoholic drinks consumed each day

This graph shows that the **incidence** of **breast cancer** is linked to both **age** and **alcohol consumption**. The graph shows that the incidence of breast cancer is **higher** in women who drink **more alcohol**. Alcohol consumption is an **environmental factor**.

1) If you only saw **one** of these graphs you may think **only genetics and age**, or **only alcohol consumption and age**, affect your **risk** of developing **breast cancer**.

2) When you look at **both sets of data** you can see that **all** these things affect the risk.

3) It's **difficult** to tell **which factor** (genes or alcohol) has the **largest effect**.

4) Also, there are **other environmental factors** that are thought to be involved in increasing the risk of developing breast cancer (e.g. **diet**, **exercise**, etc.) that aren't considered here.

Practice Questions

Q1 What is meant by the term locus?

Q2 What is meant by the term polygenic?

Exam Question

Q1 A study was conducted into how smoking during pregnancy affects the birth mass of newborn babies, depending on the genotype of the mother. The results showed that women who smoked during the entire pregnancy had babies with a mean reduction in birth mass of 377 grams. But the reduction was as much as 1285 grams among women with certain genotypes.

What can be concluded about the influence of genetic factors and environmental factors on birth mass? Give evidence from the study to support your answer.

[4 marks]

Environmental Factor — the search is on for the most talented environment...

It's amazing to think how many factors and genes influence the way we look and behave. It's the reason why we're so lovely and unique. My parents have often said they're glad they'll never have another child as 'unique' as me.

Adaptation and Evolution

Every species has a role in the environment where it lives. All the variation between organisms means that some organisms are better adapted to their role than others...

Niche is the Role of a Species Within Its Habitat

> *A habitat is where an organism lives.*

1) The **niche** a species occupies within its habitat includes:

- Its **interactions** with **other living organisms** — e.g. the organisms it eats, and those it's eaten by.
- Its **interactions** with the **non-living environment** — e.g. the oxygen an organism breathes in, and the carbon dioxide it breathes out.

3) Every species has its own **unique niche** — a niche can only be occupied by **one species**.

4) It may **look like** two species are filling the **same niche** (e.g. they're both eaten by the same species), but there'll be **slight differences** (e.g. variations in what they eat).

5) If **two species try** to occupy the **same niche**, they will **compete** with each other. One species will be **more successful** than the other, until **only one** of the species is **left**.

6) Here are a couple of examples of niches:

Common Pipistrelle Bat

This bat lives throughout Britain on **farmland**, **open woodland**, **hedgerows** and **urban areas**. It feeds by **flying** and catching **insects** using **echolocation (high-pitched sounds)** at a **frequency** of around **45 kHz**.

Soprano Pipistrelle Bat

This bat lives in Britain in **woodland** areas, close to **lakes** or **rivers**. It feeds by **flying** and catching **insects** using **echolocation**, at a **frequency** of **55 kHz**.

It may **look like** both species are filling the **same niche** (e.g. they **both eat insects**), but there are **slight differences** (e.g. they use **different frequencies** for their echolocation).

Organisms Can be Adapted to their Niche in Three Ways

1) Adaptations are features that **increase** an organism's chance of **survival** and **reproduction**.

2) All species have adaptations that allow them to **use their environment** in a way that **no other species** can — they're **adapted** for their **niche**.

3) Adaptations can be **behavioural**, **physiological** and **anatomical**:

Sid and Nancy were well adapted to hiding in candyfloss shops.

① Behavioural adaptations

Ways an organism **acts** that increase its chance of survival and reproduction. For example:
- Male common pipistrelle bats make **mating calls** to **attract** female common pipistrelle bats.

② Physiological adaptations

Processes inside an organism's body that increase its chance of survival. For example:
- Pipistrelle bats **lower their metabolism** (the chemical reactions that take place in their body) in order to **hibernate** over winter. This allows them to **conserve energy** in the months when **food** is **scarce**.

③ Anatomical adaptations

Structural features of an organism's body that increase its chance of survival. For example:
- Pipistrelle bats have **light, flexible wings** that allow them to hunt **fast-flying** insects.

Adaptation and Evolution

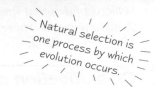

Natural selection is one process by which evolution occurs.

Adaptations Become More Common by Evolution

Useful adaptations become more common in populations of species because of **evolution** by **natural selection**:

1) Individuals within a population **show variation** in their **phenotypes** (their characteristics).

2) **Predation**, **disease** and **competition** create a **struggle for survival**.

3) Individuals with **better adaptations** (characteristics that give a selective advantage, e.g. being able to run away from predators faster) are **more likely** to **survive**, **reproduce** and **pass on** their advantageous adaptations to their **offspring**.

4) Over time, the **number** of individuals with the advantageous adaptations **increases**.

5) Over generations this leads to **evolution** as the favourable adaptations become **more common** in the population.

The explanation above is an outline of **Charles Darwin's theory of evolution** by natural selection. Over time this theory has become **increasingly accepted** as more **evidence** has been found to support it, and no evidence has been shown to disprove it. Evidence increases scientists' **confidence** in a theory — the more evidence there is, the more chance of something becoming an **accepted scientific explanation** (see page 2).

Here's an example to show you how natural selection leads to evolution:

Peppered Moths

1) Peppered moths show **variation** in **colour** — there are **light** ones and **dark** ones.

2) Before the 1800s there were **more light moths** than dark moths.

3) During the 1800s, **pollution** had **blackened** many of the trees that the moths lived on.

4) Dark coloured moths were now **better adapted** to this environment — they were better **camouflaged** from predators, so would be more likely to **survive**, reproduce and pass on their dark colouring to their offspring.

5) During this time the **number** of **dark moths increased**.

That colour is marvellous on you, really darling.

Practice Questions

Q1 How many species can occupy a single niche?

Q2 What is meant by the term adaptation?

Q3 Describe the differences between behavioural, physiological and anatomical adaptations.

Exam Questions

Q1 Describe what is meant by the term niche. [3 marks]

Q2 Hedgehogs are commonly found in gardens across the UK. They are brown with long, spiky fur, small ears and claws. They hibernate over winter and can roll into a ball when alarmed. Give one behavioural, one physiological and two anatomical adaptations of hedgehogs, and suggest how each helps them to survive. [8 marks]

Q3 Explain how natural selection can lead to adaptations becoming more common in a population. [5 marks]

CGP — the natural selection for evolving grade A students...

Hopefully the stuff about niches is a little bit clearer now. If you still can't remember what a niche is, keep copying out my lovely definition until you can see your face in it — my two batty assistants will help. And now ladies and gentlemen, for my final trick... I will make this entire page disappear... (please turn over). Niche... I mean nice.

Classification

Millions of different species have evolved over the few billion years since life began. All these species need names though, which is where classification comes in — it's about naming and organising species into groups — sounds thrilling...

Classification *is All About* Grouping Together Similar Organisms

Taxonomy is the science of classification. It involves **naming** organisms and **organising them** into **groups** based on their **similarities** and **differences**. This makes it **easier** for scientists to **identify** them and to **study** them.

1) There are **seven** levels of groups (called taxonomic groups) used in classification.

2) **Similar organisms** are first sorted into **large groups** called **kingdoms**, e.g. all animals are in the animal kingdom.

3) **Similar** organisms from that kingdom are then grouped into a **phylum**. **Similar** organisms from each phylum are then grouped into a **class**, and **so on** down the seven levels of the hierarchy.

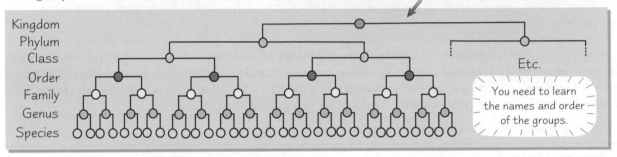

Kingdom
Phylum
Class
Order
Family
Genus
Species

Etc.

You need to learn the names and order of the groups.

4) As you move **down** the hierarchy, there are **more groups** at each level but **fewer organisms** in each group.

5) The hierarchy **ends** with **species** — the groups that contain only **one type** of organism (e.g. humans, dogs, *E. coli*). Here's the definition of a **species**:

> **A species is a group of similar organisms able to reproduce to give fertile offspring.**

All species are given a **unique scientific name** in **Latin** to **distinguish** them from similar organisms. In this **binomial (two-word)** system, the **first** word is the **genus** name and the **second** word is the **species** name — e.g. humans are *Homo sapiens*. Giving organisms a scientific name enables scientists to **communicate** about organisms in a standard way that **minimises confusion** — all scientists, in all countries, will call a species by the **same name**.

6) The **more similar** organisms are to each other the **more groups** they're in **together** as you go down the hierarchy. E.g. lions (*Panthera leo*) and tigers (*Panthera tigris*) are **different species** but they're in **all** the other, **higher** taxonomic groups together — same genus, same family, same order, etc.

7) Species in the **same genus** can be **very similar**, with similar **features** or **behaviours**, but they're **separate** species because they **can't breed together** to produce **fertile offspring** (e.g. lions and tigers can't produce fertile offspring).

Organisms *Can be Placed into One of* Five Kingdoms

See pages 44-45 for more on prokaryotes and eukaryotes. — Remember — eukaryotic cells have DNA contained within a nucleus.

All organisms can be placed into one of **five kingdoms** based on their **general features**:

KINGDOM	EXAMPLES	FEATURES
Prokaryotae (Monera)	bacteria	prokaryotes, unicellular (single-celled), no nucleus, less than 5 μm
Protoctista	algae, protozoa	eukaryotic cells, usually live in water, single-celled or simple multicellular organisms
Fungi	moulds, yeasts, mushrooms	eukaryotic, chitin cell wall, saprotrophic (absorb substances from dead or decaying organisms)
Plantae	mosses, ferns, flowering plants	eukaryotic, multicellular, cell walls made of cellulose, can photosynthesise, contain chlorophyll, autotrophic (produce their own food)
Animalia	nematodes (roundworms), molluscs, insects, fish, reptiles, birds, mammals	eukaryotic, multicellular, no cell walls, heterotrophic (consume plants and animals)

Classification

New Scientific Data Can Lead to New Taxonomic Groupings

1) Species are classified into taxonomic groups based on **loads of things**, e.g. what they **look like**, their **physiology** and **how related they are**.

2) **New data** about any of these things can influence the way species are **classified**.

3) New data has to be **evaluated** by other scientists though (to check it's **OK**). If scientists generally agree with the new data, it can lead to an **organism** being **reclassified** or lead to changes in the **classification system structure**.

4) This shows the **tentative nature** of scientific knowledge — it's always changing based on new data (see page 2).

EXAMPLE — Three Domains vs Five Kingdoms

1) A new, **three domain** classification system has been proposed based on **new data**.

2) The new data came from **molecular phylogeny**:

- **Phylogeny** is the study of the **evolutionary history** of groups of **organisms**.
- Phylogeny tells us **which species are related** to which and how **closely related** they are.
- **Molecular phylogeny** looks at **molecules** (**DNA** and **proteins**) to see how **closely related** organisms are, e.g. **more closely related** organisms have **more similar molecules**.

3) This new system classifies organisms in a **different** way:

1) In the **older**, **five kingdom** system of classification, all organisms are placed into **one** of five kingdoms.

2) In the **new**, **three domain** system all organisms are placed into one of three **domains** — **large superkingdoms** that are **above** the kingdoms in the **taxonomic hierarchy** (see previous page).

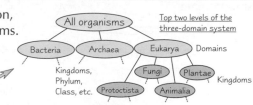

3) Organisms that were in the kingdom **Prokaryotae** (unicellular organisms **without a nucleus**) are separated into two domains — the **Archaea** and **Bacteria**. Organisms from the **other four** kingdoms (organisms with cells that **contain a nucleus**) are placed in the third domain — **Eukarya**.

4) The **Prokaryotae** were **reclassified** into **two domains** because **molecular phylogeny** suggested that archaea and bacteria are **more distantly related** than originally thought.

Practice Questions

Q1 What is taxonomy?

Q2 Give two features of organisms in the kingdom Fungi.

	Kingdom	Phylum	Class	Order	Family	Genus	Species
Humans	Animalia	Chordata	Mammalia	Primates	Hominidae	Homo	sapiens
Bonobos					Hominidae		

Exam Question

Q1 The bonobo (*Pan paniscus*) is a chimpanzee-like animal that belongs to the same family as humans — the Hominidae.

a) Complete the table above to show the classification of the bonobo. [2 marks]

b) Name four features the bonobo must have to place it in the kingdom Animalia. [4 marks]

Snozcumber kingdom features — long, thin, green, filled with snot...

Phew, after that section I think you should go and have a cup of tea to recover... Remember that classification systems can change if any new data rears its ugly mug. But don't forget that the data has to be evaluated by other scientists before it's accepted — they have to check that experiments or studies done were designed properly (to get reliable data) and that the conclusions are fair.

Plant Cell Structure and Plant Stems

Plants aren't everybody's cup of tea, but they should be — without them we'd be stuck. We get loads of useful stuff from plants, but before we delve into that there are a few important bits and pieces you need to know...

Plant Cells Have Different Organelles from Animal Cells

For more on animal organelles see p. 44-45.

You know all about the organelles in animal cells — well plant cells are a little bit different.
Plant cells contain all the organelles that animal cells do, **plus a few extras** that **animal cells don't have**:

ORGANELLE	DIAGRAM	DESCRIPTION	FUNCTION
Cell wall	cell membrane / cell wall / cytoplasm	A rigid structure that surrounds **plant cells**. It's made mainly of the carbohydrate **cellulose**.	**Supports** plant cells.
Middle lamella	middle lamella / cell A / cell B / cell wall	The **outermost layer** of the cell.	This layer acts as an **adhesive**, sticking adjacent plant cells together. It gives the plant **stability**.
Plasmodesmata	plasmodesma (plural = plasmodesmata) / cell A / cell B / cell wall	**Channels** in the cell walls that **link** adjacent cells together.	Allow **transport** of **substances** and **communication** between cells.
Pits	pits / cell A / cell B / cell wall	Regions of the cell wall where the wall is **very thin**. They're arranged in **pairs** — the pit in one cell is lined up with the pit in the adjacent cell.	Allow **transport** of **substances** between cells.
Chloroplast	stroma / two membranes / granum (plural = grana) / lamella (plural = lamellae)	A small, **flattened** structure. It's surrounded by a **double membrane**, and also has membranes inside called **thylakoid membranes**. These membranes are stacked up in some parts of the chloroplast to form **grana**. Grana are linked together by lamellae — thin, flat pieces of thylakoid membrane.	The **site** where **photosynthesis** takes place. Some parts of photosynthesis happen in the **grana**, and other parts happen in the **stroma** (a thick fluid found in chloroplasts).
Amyloplast	starch grain / membrane	A small organelle enclosed by a **membrane**. They contain **starch granules**.	**Storage** of **starch grains** (see p. 7). They also convert starch back to glucose for release when the plant requires it.
Vacuole and Tonoplast	vacuole / tonoplast / plant cell	The vacuole is a **compartment** surrounded by a **membrane** called the **tonoplast**.	The vacuole contains the **cell sap**, which is made up of water, enzymes, minerals and waste products. Vacuoles keep the cells **turgid** — this stops plants wilting. They're also involved in the **breakdown** and **isolation** of unwanted chemicals in the cell. The tonoplast controls what **enters** and **leaves** the vacuole.

Plant Cell Structure and Plant Stems

Different Parts of Plant Stems have Different Functions

Plant stems are made up of loads of different things — the only bits you need to
worry about are **xylem vessels** and **sclerenchyma fibres**.

Xylem vessels

1) The function of xylem vessels is to **transport water**
   and **mineral ions** up the plant, and **provide support**.

2) They're very **long**, **tube-like** structures formed from **dead cells**,
   joined end to end. The tubes are found together in **bundles**.

3) The cells are **longer** than they are **wide**, they have a **hollow
   lumen** (they contain **no cytoplasm**) and have **no end walls**.

4) This makes an **uninterrupted tube**, allowing water and
   mineral ions to pass up through the middle easily.

5) Their walls are **thickened** with a **woody** substance
   called **lignin**, which helps to **support** the plant.

6) **Water** and **mineral ions** move **into** and **out of** the vessels through **pits** in the walls where there's **no lignin**.

7) Xylem vessels are found throughout the plant but particularly around the **centre of the stem**,
   where they group together with other vessels to form **vascular bundles**.

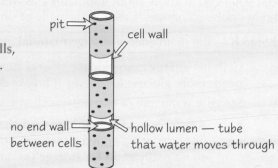

pit → cell wall

no end wall between cells → hollow lumen — tube that water moves through

Stem cross-section

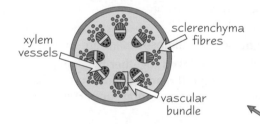

xylem vessels — sclerenchyma fibres — vascular bundle

Sclerenchyma fibres

1) The function of sclerenchyma fibres is to provide **support**.

2) Like xylem vessels, they're also made of bundles of
   dead cells that run vertically up the stem.

3) The cells are **longer** than they are **wide**, and also have
   a **hollow lumen** and **end walls**.

4) Their cell walls are also **thickened** with **lignin**. They have
   more **cellulose** (see next page) than other plant cells.

5) They're usually associated with the **vascular bundles**.

Practice Questions

Q1 Which two organelles allow transport of substances between plant cells?

Q2 What is the function of chloroplasts?

Q3 What is the function of amyloplasts?

Q4 Name the membrane that surrounds the vacuole.

Exam Question

Q1 a) The image on the right shows a cross-section of
   a plant stem as seen under a light microscope.
   Identify the structures labelled X and Y. [2 marks]

   b) Compare the structure and function of the
   two structures you have named above. [9 marks]

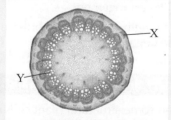

Dr Keith Wheeler/Science Photo Library

Esmerelda... the cells! the cells!

*I know the table of organelles looks pretty daunting, but I'm afraid you've got to learn it — scribble down one diagram at
a time and write out its description and function 'til you know it like the back of your hand. As for plant stems, they aren't
too tricky — just make sure you can compare the structure and function of xylem vessels and sclerenchyma fibres.*

Starch, Cellulose and Fibres

I know these pages don't have the most stimulating title, but they're actually pretty interesting... honest...

The **Structures** of **Starch** and **Cellulose** Determine Their **Functions**

You might remember some stuff about the structure of **starch** from Unit 1.
Well you need to know about it for Unit 2 as well — but now you've got to **compare** it to **cellulose**, another polysaccharide. Cellulose is made of similar stuff, but has a **different function**.

1) Starch — the main **energy storage material** in **plants**

1) Cells get **energy** from **glucose**. Plants **store** excess glucose as **starch** (when a plant **needs more glucose** for energy it **breaks down** starch to release the glucose).

2) Starch is a mixture of **two** polysaccharides of **alpha-glucose** — **amylose** and **amylopectin**:

- **Amylose** — a long, **unbranched chain** of α–glucose. The angles of the glycosidic bonds give it a **coiled structure**, almost like a cylinder. This makes it **compact**, so it's really **good for storage** because you can **fit more in** to a small space.

- **Amylopectin** — a long, **branched chain** of α–glucose. Its **side branches** allow the **enzymes** that break down the molecule to get at the **glycosidic bonds easily**. This means that the glucose can be **released quickly**.

3) Starch is **insoluble** in water, so it doesn't cause water to enter cells by **osmosis** (which would make them swell). This makes it good for **storage**.

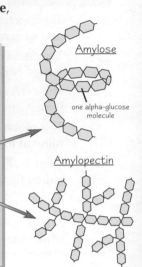

Amylose

one alpha-glucose molecule

Amylopectin

2) Cellulose — the major component of **cell walls** in **plants**

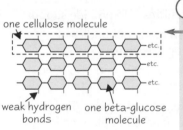

one cellulose molecule

weak hydrogen bonds   one beta-glucose molecule

1) Cellulose is made of **long, unbranched** chains of **beta-glucose**, joined by **glycosidic bonds**.

2) The glycosidic bonds are **straight**, so the cellulose chains are straight.

3) Between **50 and 80** cellulose chains are **linked together** by a large number of **hydrogen bonds** to form **strong threads** called **microfibrils**. The strong threads mean cellulose provides **structural support** for cells (e.g. they strengthen plant cell walls).

See page 6 for more on glycosidic bonds.

Plant Fibres are **Useful** to **Humans** Because They're **Strong**

1) Plant fibres are made up of **long tubes** of **plant cells**, e.g. sclerenchyma fibres are made of tubes of dead cells.

2) They're **strong**, which makes them useful for loads of things, e.g. **ropes** or **fabrics** like hemp.

3) They're strong for a **number of reasons**, but you only need to know **two**:

The arrangement of cellulose microfibrils in the cell wall

1) The cell wall contains **cellulose microfibrils** in a **net-like arrangement**.

2) The strength of the microfibrils and their arrangement in the cell wall gives plant fibres **strength**.

cell membrane   secondary cell wall   normal cell wall

layer of cellulose microfibrils in cell wall

The secondary thickening of cell walls

1) When some structural plant cells (like sclerenchyma) have finished growing, they produce a **secondary cell wall** between the normal cell wall and the cell membrane.

2) The secondary cell wall is **thicker** than the normal cell wall and usually has **more lignin**.

3) The growth of a secondary cell wall is called **secondary thickening**.

4) Secondary thickening makes plant fibres even **stronger**.

Starch, Cellulose and Fibres

You Can Measure the **Tensile Strength** of **Plant Fibres**

The **tensile strength** of a fibre is the **maximum load** it can take before it **breaks**. Knowing the tensile strength of plant fibres can be really important, especially if they're going to be used for things like ropes (e.g. a rock climber would want to know the rope they're using is going to hold their weight). Here's how you'd find out the tensile strength of a plant fibre:

I don't know Dave, we usually use weights to test tensile strength...

1) Attach the fibre to a **clamp stand** and **hang** a **weight** from the other end.

2) Keep **adding weights**, one at a time, until the **fibre breaks**.

3) Record the **mass needed** to break the fibre — the **higher** the mass, the **higher** the tensile strength.

4) **Repeat** the experiment with different samples of the same fibre — this increases the **reliability**.

5) The fibres being tested should always be the **same length**.

6) Throughout the experiment all **other variables**, like temperature and humidity, must be kept **constant**.

7) You also need to take **safety measures** when doing this experiment, e.g. wear goggles to protect your eyes, and leave the area where the weights will fall clear so they don't squish your toes.

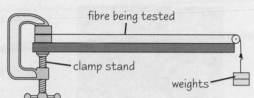

fibre being tested
clamp stand
weights

Practice Questions

Q1   Name the two polysaccharides that starch is made up from.

Q2   Compare the structure and function of starch and cellulose.

Q3   What is meant by tensile strength?

Exam Questions

Q1   The physical properties of plant fibres can make them useful to humans.

a) Describe the arrangement of cellulose microfibrils in a plant cell wall, and explain how this relates to the properties of plant fibres.   [4 marks]

b) Describe secondary thickening of plant cell walls, and explain how this relates to the properties of plant fibres.   [4 marks]

Q2   A group of students investigated the tensile strength of four different plant fibres. Their results are displayed in the table on the right.

	fibre A	fibre B	fibre C	fibre D
length of fibre / cm	60	60	60	60
mass which caused fibre to break / kg	3.5	220.0	52.7	17.2

a) Describe a method they could have used to obtain these results.   [8 marks]

b) Based on this information, which fibre would be most suitable to make a climbing rope? Explain your answer.   [2 marks]

The world's strongest plant — live from the Bahamas...

Well at least there are lots of pretty pictures on these pages to look at. Anyway, it's not so bad — basically plant fibres are really strong and there are lots of reasons, but you just need to know about how the cell walls are strong, which makes the plant fibres super strong. They're strong to the finish, 'cos they eats their spinach...

Sustainability and Plant Minerals

So, you can use plants to make ropes and fabrics, but there are plenty of other groovy things you can make from plants, like plastics, fuel and castles of mashed potatoes. Making things from plants is also sustainable, which is nice...

Sustainable Practices Don't Deplete Resources

1) Sustainability is all about **using resources** in a way that meets the **needs** of the **present generation** without messing it up for **future generations** (i.e. not using something up so there's none left).

2) To **make products sustainably** you have to use **renewable resources**.

3) Renewable resources are resources that can be **used indefinitely** without **running out**, e.g. **plants** are a renewable resource because harvested plants can be **regrown** (so there'll be plenty for future generations). **Fossil fuels** (e.g. petrol) are **not** a renewable resource — once you've used it all there's no more.

If only Amy's sweets were a renewable resource...

4) An example of a **sustainable practice** is replacing trees after logging. Whenever a tree is cut down, a **new one** is planted in its place. When the tree is fully grown the process can **begin again** — the environment isn't **significantly damaged** in the long term.

5) **Unsustainable practices** can't continue indefinitely. The **resources** would eventually **run out**.

6) An example of an unsustainable practice is the use of **fossil fuels** to make oil-based plastics like polythene.

Using Plant Fibres and Starch can Contribute to Sustainability

Plant fibres

1) **Ropes** and **fabrics** can be made of **plastic**, which is made from **oil**. They can also be made from **plant fibres** (see page 66).

2) Making products from plant fibres is **more sustainable** than making them from oil — **less fossil fuel** is **used up**, and crops can be **regrown** to **maintain the supply** for future generations.

3) Products made from plant fibres are **biodegradable** — they can be broken down by **microbes**, unlike most oil-based plastics (which can't be broken down and remain in the environment for many years).

4) Plants are **easier to grow** and **process** (to extract the fibres) than extracting and processing oil. This makes them **cheaper** and it's easier to do in developing countries (as less technology and expertise is needed).

One disadvantage of making ropes from plant fibres is that they're generally not as strong as ropes made of plastic.

Starch

1) Starch is found in **all plants** — crops such as **potatoes** and **corn** are particularly rich in starch.

2) **Plastics** are usually made from **oil**, but some can be made from **plant-based** materials, like **starch**. These plastics are called **bioplastics**.

3) Making plastics from starch is **more sustainable** than making them from oil because less fossil fuel is used up and the **crops** from which the starch came from can be **regrown**.

4) **Vehicle fuel** is also usually made from **oil**, but you can make fuel from **starch**. E.g. **bioethanol** is a fuel that can be made from starch.

5) Making fuel from starch is **more sustainable** than making it from oil because, you guessed it, **less fossil fuel** is used up and the **crops** from which the starch came from can be **regrown**.

The potatoes were getting worried about all this talk of using more starch — you could see it in their eyes.

Sustainability and Plant Minerals

Plants **Need Water** and **Inorganic Ions**

Plants need **water** and **inorganic ions** (**minerals**) for a number of different functions. They're absorbed through the **roots** and travel through the plant in the xylem. If there isn't enough water or inorganic ions in the soil, the plant will show **deficiency symptoms**, like stunted growth. You need to know why plants need water and these three minerals:

- <u>Water</u> is needed for **photosynthesis**, to maintain **structural rigidity**, **transport minerals** and **regulate temperature**.
- <u>Magnesium ions</u> are needed for the production of **chlorophyll** — the **pigment** needed for **photosynthesis**.
- <u>Nitrate ions</u> are needed for the production of **DNA**, **proteins** (including enzymes) and **chlorophyll**. They're required for **plant growth**, **fruit production** and **seed production**.
- <u>Calcium ions</u> are important components in plant **cell walls**. They're required for **plant growth**.

You Can **Investigate Plant Mineral Deficiencies** in the **Lab**

Here's how to **investigate mineral deficiency** in a plant using calcium ions as an example
(you could do the same experiment with any of the minerals mentioned above):

Method

1) Take 30 seedlings of the **same plant** (they should be the **same age** and **height**) and plant them in **separate pots**.

2) Make up three **nutrient broths** containing all the essential minerals, but vary the concentration of **calcium ions**. Make up one broth with a **high** concentration, one with a **medium** concentration and one with a **low** concentration of calcium.

3) Split the plants into three groups. Each group should be given **only one** of the three broths.

4) Record the **heights** of the plants after seven weeks. Calculate the **average height** of each group of plants.

5) During the experiment it's important to keep all other **variables the same**, e.g. the amount of sunlight and water the plants receive.

Results

1) The **greater** the concentration of calcium, the **more** the plants grew — average heights of 12, 18 and 23 cm were reached for plants given low, medium and high concentrations respectively.

2) This shows that when calcium is **deficient**, plant growth is **inhibited**.

Calcium ion concentration	Average height at start / cm	Average height after 7 weeks / cm
High	6	23
Medium	6	18
Low	6	12

Practice Questions

Q1 What does it mean if a product is made sustainably?

Q2 Suggest two advantages of using plant fibres rather than oil-based plastics to make rope.

Q3 Name two products, other than rope, that can be made from plants.

Exam Question

Q1 Describe an experiment you could carry out to investigate the effects of nitrate deficiency on a plant. [6 marks]

Potatoes, good for plastics and fuel — we'll be eating them next...

*Renewable resources are great — they'll never run out (like my bad jokes — plenty more where they came from...).
There's another experiment to learn here, but look at it like this — tonnes more cheap marks in the exam, 'cos when they ask
you to describe an experiment you get loads for it. Now, doesn't that just make you want to copy it out a few times...*

Drug Testing and Drugs from Plants

A lot of drugs come from plants. Nowadays it's seen as a good idea to test drugs before we use them. But back in the olden days drug testing tended to be a bit hit and miss...

Testing Drugs Used to be Trial and Error

Before **new drugs** become available to the general public they need to be **tested** — to make sure they **work** and don't have any horrible **side effects**. In the past, drug testing was a lot **less scientific** than modern clinical trials (see below) and a bit more dangerous for the participants...

Example — William Withering's digitalis soup

1) **William Withering** was a scientist in the 1700s.

2) He discovered that an extract of **foxgloves** could be used to treat **dropsy** (swelling brought about by heart failure). This extract contained the drug **digitalis**.

3) Withering made a **chance observation** — a patient suffering from dropsy made a good recovery after being treated with a **traditional remedy** containing foxgloves. Withering knew foxgloves were **poisonous**, so he started testing **different versions** of the remedy with **different concentrations** of digitalis — this became known as his **digitalis soup**.

4) **Too much** digitalis **poisoned** his patients, while **too little** had **no effect**.

5) It was through this crude method of **trial and error** that he discovered the right amount to give to a patient.

Modern Drug Testing is More Rigorous

1) Nowadays **drug testing protocols** are much more **controlled**.

2) Before a drug is tried on any live subjects, computers are used to **model** the **potential effects**.

3) Tests are also carried out on **human tissues** in a **lab**, then they're tested on **live animals** before **clinical trials** are carried out on **humans**.

4) During clinical trials new drugs undergo **three phases of testing**. This involves three different stages, with more people at each stage:

Drugs that pass all three phases are considered for clinical use.

Phase 1 — This involves testing a new drug on a **small group** of **healthy individuals**. It's done to find out things like **safe dosage**, if there are any **side effects**, and how the body **reacts** to the drug.

Phase 2 — If a drug passes Phase 1 it will then be tested on a **larger group of people** (this time **patients**) to see **how well** the drug actually **works**.

Phase 3 — During this phase the drug is **compared** to **existing treatments**. It involves testing the drug on **hundreds**, or even **thousands**, of patients. Patients are randomly split into two groups — one group receives the **new treatment** and the other group receives the **existing treatment**. This allows scientists to tell if the new drug is **any better** than existing drugs.

Dirk carried on, blissfully unaware that drug testing was more rigorous these days.

Using **placebos** and a **double blind study design** make the results of clinical trials **more reliable**.

Placebos

In Phase 2 clinical trials the patients are split into **two groups**. One group is given the drug and the other is given a **placebo** — an **inactive substance** that looks exactly like the drug but doesn't actually do anything. Patients often show a **placebo effect** — where they show some improvement because they **believe** that they're receiving treatment. Giving half the patients a placebo allows researchers to see if the **drug actually works** (if it improves patients more than the placebo does).

Double blind study design

Phase 2 and 3 clinical trials are usually **double blind** — **neither** the **patients** nor the **doctors** know who's been given the new drug and who's been given the placebo (or old drug). This **reduces bias** in the results because the **attitudes** of the patients and doctors **can't affect the results**. E.g. if a doctor knows someone has received the real drug, they may think they've improved more than they actually have — but if they don't know this can't happen.

Drug Testing and Drugs from Plants

Some Plants Have **Antimicrobial Properties**

Some plants have **antimicrobial properties** — they **kill** or **inhibit the growth** of microorganisms.
You need to know how to investigate the antimicrobial properties of plants — here's an example:

1) Take **extracts** from the plants **you want to test**. To do this you need to **dry** and **grind** each plant, then soak them in **ethanol** (the ethanol acts as a solvent). The plants should all be the **same size**, so the amount of extract is the same.

2) **Filter off** the **liquid bit** (the ethanol containing the dissolved plant extract).

3) You need some **bacteria** to test the plant extract on — evenly spread a sample of bacteria onto an **agar** (nutrient) **plate**.

4) Dip discs of **absorbent paper** in the extracts. The discs of paper should all be the **same size** so they absorb the same volume of liquid.

5) You also need to do a **control disc** soaked only in ethanol (to make sure it isn't the ethanol or the paper that's inhibiting bacterial growth).

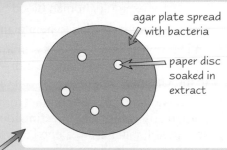

agar plate spread with bacteria

paper disc soaked in extract

6) Place the paper discs on the agar plate — make sure they're spread out.

7) **Incubate** the plate to allow the bacteria to **grow**.

8) Where the bacteria **can't grow** there'll be a **clear patch** in the lawn of bacteria. This is called an **inhibition zone**.

9) The size of an **inhibition zone** tells you how well the antimicrobial plant extract is working. The **larger** the zone, the **more** effective the plant extract is.

Here's an example of the kind of results you might get:

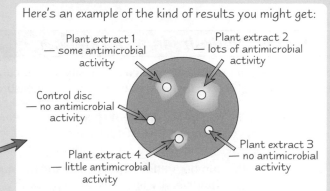

Plant extract 1 — some antimicrobial activity

Plant extract 2 — lots of antimicrobial activity

Control disc — no antimicrobial activity

Plant extract 4 — little antimicrobial activity

Plant extract 3 — no antimicrobial activity

Practice Questions

Q1 Give one way that modern drug testing differs from historic drug testing.

Q2 What is a placebo?

Q3 What is a double blind trial?

Exam Questions

Q1 Describe how William Withering discovered and tested the drug digitalis. [5 marks]

Q2 Plant extracts have long been used to relieve symptoms of many diseases.

a) Describe how you could conduct an experiment to discover
if a plant species had antibacterial properties. [10 marks]

b) A new drug made from a plant extract would have to go through clinical trials
before it's made available to patients. Describe this process. [7 marks]

Digitalis soup — like Alphabetti Spaghetti with numbers...

Drug testing these days is really quite complicated, what with all this three phase testing and placebos. Though if you ask me, anything that's double blind just sounds like a recipe for disaster. Anyway, make sure you can talk about the differences between past and present drug testing, and that you know how to test the antimicrobial properties of plants.

Biodiversity and Endemism

Bet you've noticed how there are loads of different living things in the world — well that's biodiversity in a nutshell. What's even more nutty is that scientists quite like to measure it. There's no accounting for taste...

Biodiversity is the Variety of Organisms

1) **Biodiversity** is the **variety** of **living organisms** in an **area**. It includes:
   - **Species diversity** — the number of **different species** and the **abundance** of each species in an **area**. For example, a wood could contain many different species of plants, insects, birds and mammals.
   - **Genetic diversity** — the variation of **alleles within a species** (or a population of a species). For example, human blood type is determined by a gene with four different alleles.

2) **Conservation** is needed to **help maintain** biodiversity (see p. 74).

3) **Endemism** is when a species is **unique** to a **single place** (isn't naturally found anywhere else in the world) — e.g. the **giant tortoise** is **endemic** to the Galapagos Islands — it can only be found there.

4) Conservation is really important for endemic species because they're particularly **vulnerable to extinction**. They're only found in one place, so if their habitat is threatened they can't usually migrate and their **numbers** will **decline**.

Sarah was endemic to the shopping centre — she could only be found there.

The Species Diversity in a Habitat can be Measured

It's important to be able to **measure species diversity** so you can **compare different habitats**, or study how a habitat has **changed over time**. You can measure species diversity in different ways:

1) Count the number of **different species** in an area. The number of different species in the area is called the **species richness**. The **higher** the number of species, the **greater** the species richness. But species richness gives **no indication** of the **abundance** of each species.

2) Count the number of **different species** <u>and</u> the number of **individuals in each species**. Then use a **biodiversity index** (worked out with a fancy equation, e.g. **Simpson's Index of Diversity**) to **calculate** the species diversity. This takes into account the **number and abundance** of each species.

When measuring species diversity, it's usually **too time-consuming** to count every individual organism in a habitat. Instead, a **sample** of the population is taken. **Estimates** about the whole habitat are based on the sample. Here's what sampling involves:

1) Choose an area to **sample** — a small area within the habitat being studied.

2) To avoid **bias** in your results, the sample should be **random**. For example, if you were investigating the species of plants in a field you could pick random sample sites by dividing the field into a **grid** and using a **random number generator** to select coordinates.

3) **Count** the number of individuals of **each species** in the sample area. How you do this depends on **what** you're counting, for example:

   - For plants you'd use a **quadrat** (a frame which you place on the ground).
   - For flying insects you'd use a **sweepnet** (a net on a pole).
   - For ground insects you'd use a **pitfall trap** (a small pit that insects can't get out of).
   - For aquatic animals you'd use a **net**.

4) **Repeat** the process — take as many samples as possible. This gives a better indication of the **whole habitat**.

5) Use the results to **estimate** the **total number of individuals** or the **total number of different species** (the species richness) in the habitat being studied.

6) When sampling **different habitats** and comparing them, always use the **same sampling technique**.

Biodiversity and Endemism

The **Genetic Diversity** within a **Species** can also be **Measured**

You can measure diversity **within a species** by looking at **genetic diversity**.

1) Diversity within a species is the **variety** shown by **individuals** of that species (or within a population of that species).

2) Individuals of the **same species** vary because they have **different alleles** (different versions of the same gene, see page 38).

3) Genetic diversity is the **variety of alleles** in the **gene pool** of a species (or population).

4) The **gene pool** is the **complete set of alleles** in a species (or population).

5) The **greater the variety** of alleles, the **greater** the genetic diversity. For example, animals have different alleles for **blood group**. In humans there are **three alleles** for blood group, but gorillas have **only one**, so humans show **greater genetic diversity** for blood group than gorillas.

6) You can investigate the **changes** in the genetic diversity of a population over time, or how two populations of the same species show **different diversity**.

To measure the genetic diversity of a species you can look at **two things**:

① Phenotype

1) Phenotype describes the **observable characteristics** of an **organism**.

2) **Different alleles** code for slightly **different versions** of the same characteristics.

3) By looking at the different phenotypes in a population of a species, you can get an idea of the **diversity of alleles** in that population.

4) The **larger the number** of different phenotypes, the **greater** the genetic diversity.

5) For example, humans have **different eye colours** due to **different alleles**. Humans in northern Europe show a **variety** of blue, grey, green or brown eyes. Outside this area, eye colour shows **little variety** — they're **usually brown**. There's **greater genetic diversity** in eye colour in northern Europe.

② Genotype

1) Samples of an organism's DNA can be taken and the sequence of **base pairs analysed** (see p. 34).

2) The **order of bases** in different alleles is **slightly different**, e.g. the allele for brown hair will have a slightly different order of bases than the allele for blonde hair.

3) By sequencing the DNA of individuals of the same species, you can look at **similarities** and **differences** in the alleles within a species.

4) You can measure the **number of different alleles** a species has for one characteristic to see how **genetically diverse** the species is.

5) The **larger the number** of different alleles, the **greater** the genetic diversity.

Practice Questions

Q1 What is biodiversity?

Q2 What is species richness?

Q3 What is meant by the term gene pool?

Exam Question

Q1 There are several species of finch that are only found on the Hawaiian islands.

a) What word is used to describe a species that only exists in one place? [1 mark]

b) Describe one way you could measure the biodiversity of finches within a single habitat and one way you could measure biodiversity within a single finch species. [2 marks]

Species richness — goldfish and money spiders top the list...

I know endemism sounds like some sort of disease, but it's not so painful really. Knowing these terms is important cos they're easy marks in the exam — so write out the definitions for biodiversity and endemism a few times. The trickier stuff is all this genetic diversity jazz, so read the examples I've given carefully — they'll help you to understand the text.

How to Interpret Experiment and Study Data

Science is all about getting good evidence to test your theories... so scientists need to be able to spot a badly designed experiment or study a mile off, and be able to interpret the results of an experiment or study properly. Being the cheeky little monkeys they are, your exam board will want to make sure you can do it too. Here's a quick reference section to show you how to go about interpreting data-style questions.

Here Are Some **Things** You Might be **Asked** to do...

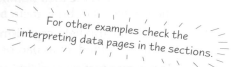
For other examples check the interpreting data pages in the sections.

Here are two examples of the kind of data you could expect to get:

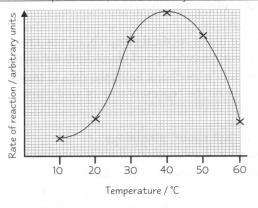

Experiment A

Experiment A examined the effect of temperature on the rate of an enzyme-controlled reaction. The rate of reaction for enzyme X was measured at six different temperatures (from 10 to 60 °C). All other variables were kept constant. A negative control containing all solutions except the enzyme was included. The rate of reaction for the negative control was zero at each temperature used. The results are shown in the graph below.

Study B

Study B examined the effect of farm hedgerow length on the number of species in a given area. The number of species present during a single week on 12 farms was counted by placing ground-level traps. All the farms were a similar area. The traps were left out every day, at 6 am for two hours and once again at 6 pm for two hours. The data was plotted against hedgerow length. The results are shown in the scattergram below.

1) Describe the Data

You need to be able to **describe** any data you're given. The level of **detail** in your answer should be appropriate for the **number of marks** given. Loads of marks = more detail, few marks = less detail.
For the two examples above:

Example — Experiment A

1) The data shows that the **rate of reaction increases** as **temperature increases** up to a **certain point**. The rate of reaction then **decreases** as temperature increases (2 marks).

2) The data shows that the rate of reaction **increases** as temperature increases from **10 °C** up to **40 °C**. The rate of reaction then **decreases** as temperature increases from **40 °C** to **60 °C** (4 marks).

Example — Study B

The data shows a **positive correlation** between the length of hedgerows and the number of species in the area (1 mark).

Correlation describes the **relationship** between two variables — the one that's been changed and the one that's been measured. Data can show **three** types of correlation:

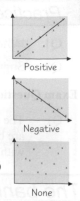

1) **Positive** — as one variable **increases** the other **increases**.

2) **Negative** — as one variable **increases** the other **decreases**.

3) **None** — there is **no relationship** between the two variables.

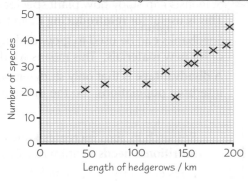

How to Interpret Experiment and Study Data

2) Draw or Check the Conclusions

1) Ideally, only **two** quantities would ever change in any experiment or study — everything else would be **constant**.

2) If you can keep everything else constant and the results show a correlation then you **can** conclude that the change in one variable **does cause** the change in the other. ➡

3) But usually all the variables **can't** be controlled, so other **factors** (that you **couldn't** keep constant) could be having an **effect**.

4) Because of this, scientists have to be very careful when **drawing conclusions**. Most results show a **link** (correlation) between the variables, but that **doesn't prove that a change in one causes the change in the other**. ➡

5) The **data** should always **support** the conclusion. This may sound obvious but it's easy to **jump** to conclusions. Conclusions have to be **precise** — not make sweeping generalisations. ➡

Example — Experiment A

All other variables were **kept constant**. E.g. pH, enzyme concentration and substrate concentration **stayed the same** each time, so these **couldn't** have influenced the change in the rate of reaction. So you **can say** that an increase in temperature **causes** an increase in the rate of reaction up to a certain point.

Example — Study B

The length of hedgerows shows a **positive correlation** with the number of species in that area. But you **can't** conclude that fewer hedgerows **causes** fewer species. **Other factors** may have been involved, e.g. the number of **predators** of the species studied may have increased in some areas, the farmers may have used **more pesticide** in one area, or something else you hadn't thought of could have caused the pattern...

Example — Experiment A

A science magazine **concluded** from this data that enzyme X works best at **40 °C**. The data **doesn't** support this. The enzyme **could** work best at 42 °C, or 47 °C but you can't tell from the data because **increases** of **10 °C** at a time were used. The rates of reaction at in-between temperatures **weren't** measured.

3) Comment on the Reliability of the Results

Reliable means the results can be **consistently reproduced** in independent experiments. And if the results are reproducible they're more likely to be **true**. If the data isn't reliable for whatever reason you **can't draw** a valid **conclusion**. Here are some of the things that affect the reliability of data:

1) <u>Size of the data set</u> — For experiments, the **more repeats** you do, the **more reliable** the data. If you get the **same result** twice, it could be the correct answer. But if you get the same result **20 times**, it's much more reliable. The general rule for **studies** is the **larger** the sample size, the more **reliable** the **data** is.

Davina wasn't sure she'd got a large enough sample size.

E.g. Study B is quite **small** — they only used 12 farms. The **trend** shown by the data may not appear if you studied **50 or 100 farms**, or studied them for a longer period of time.

2) <u>Variables</u> — The **more variables** you **control**, the **more reliable** your data is. In an experiment you would control all the variables, but when doing a study this isn't always possible. You try to control **as many as possible** or use **matched groups** (see page 3).

E.g. ideally, all the farms in Study B would have a similar **type** of land, similar **weather**, have the same **crops** growing, etc. Then you could be more sure that the one factor being **investigated** (hedgerows) is having an **effect** on the thing being **measured** (number of species). In Experiment A, **all** other variables were controlled, e.g. pH, concentrations, volumes, so you can be sure the temperature is causing the **change** in the **reaction rate**.

Jane rarely ate chocolate, honestly.

3) <u>Data collection</u> — think about all the **problems** with the **method** and see if **bias** has slipped in. For example, members of the public sometimes tell **little porkies**, so it's easy for studies involving **questionnaires** to be biased. E.g. people often underestimate how much alcohol they drink or how many cigarettes they smoke.

E.g. in Study B, the traps were placed on the **ground**, so species like birds weren't included. The traps weren't left overnight, so **nocturnal** animals wouldn't get counted, etc. This could have affected the results.

How to Interpret Experiment and Study Data

4) **Controls** — without controls, it's very difficult to **draw valid conclusions**. **Negative controls** are used to make sure that nothing you're doing in the experiment has an effect, **other than** what you're testing. But it's not always possible to have controls in studies (study controls usually involve a group where **nothing changes**, e.g. a group of patients aren't given a new long-term treatment to make sure any effects detected in the patients having the treatment aren't due to the fact that they've had two months to recover).

E.g. in Experiment A, the **negative control** contained everything from the experiment **except** the enzyme. This was used to show that the change in reaction rate was caused by the effect of **temperature** on the **enzyme**, and nothing else. If something else in the experiment (e.g. the water, or something in the test tube) was causing the change, you would get the **same results** in the negative control (and you'd know something was up).

5) **Repetition by other scientists** — for theories to become accepted as 'fact' other scientists need to **repeat** the work (see page 2). If **multiple studies** or **experiments** come to the same conclusion, then that conclusion is **more reliable**.

E.g. if a second group of scientists carried out the same experiment for enzyme X and got the same results, the results would be **more reliable**.

4) Analyse the Data

Sometimes it's easier to **compare data** by making a few calculations first, e.g. converting raw data into **ratios** or **percentages**.

Example **Three** UK hospitals have been trying out three **different methods** to **control the spread** of chest infections. A study investigated the number of people suffering from chest infections in those hospitals over a **three month period**. The table opposite shows the results. If you just look at the **number of cases** in the **last month** (March) then the method of hospital 3 appears to have worked **least well**, as they have the **highest number** of infections. But if you look at the **percentage increase** in infections you get a different picture: hospital 1 = 30%, hospital 2 = 293%, and hospital 3 = 18%. So hospital 3 has the lowest percentage increase, suggesting their method of control is **working the best**.

	Number of cases per 6000 patients		
Hospital	Jan	Feb	March
1	60	65	78
2	14	24	55
3	93	96	110

Calculating percentage increase, hospital 1:

$$\frac{(78 - 60)}{60} \times 100 = \frac{18}{60} \times 100 = 30\%$$

There Are a Few Technical Terms You Need to Understand

I'm sure you probably know these all off by heart, but it's easy to get mixed up sometimes. So here's a quick recap of some words **commonly used** when assessing and analysing experiments and studies:

1) **Variable** — A variable is a **quantity** that has the **potential to change**, e.g. weight. There are two types of variable commonly referred to in experiments:
   - **Independent variable** — the thing that's **changed** in an experiment.
   - **Dependent variable** — the thing that you **measure** in an experiment.

*When drawing graphs, the dependent variable should go on the **y-axis** (the vertical axis) and the independent on the **x-axis** (the horizontal axis).*

2) **Accurate** — Accurate results are those that are **really close** to the **true** answer.

3) **Precise results** — These are results taken using **sensitive instruments** that measure in **small increments**, e.g. pH measured with a meter (pH 7.692) will be **more precise** than pH measured with paper (pH 8).

*It's possible for results to be precise **but not** accurate, e.g. a balance that weighs to 1/1000 th of a gram will give precise results, but if it's not **calibrated** properly the results won't be accurate.*

4) **Qualitative** — A **qualitative** test tells you **what's** present, e.g. an acid or an alkali.

5) **Quantitative** — A **quantitative** test tells you **how much** is present, e.g. an acid that's pH 2.46.

Controls — I think I prefer the remote kind...

*These pages should give you a fair idea of the points to think about when interpreting data. Just use your head and remember the three main points in the checklist — **d**escribe the **d**ata, **c**heck the **c**onclusions and make sure the **r**esults are **r**eliable.*

Answers

Unit 1: Section 1 — Biological Molecules

Page 5 — Water

1   Maximum of 3 marks available.
Water molecules have two hydrogen atoms and one oxygen atom *[1 mark]*. The hydrogen and oxygen are joined by shared electrons *[1 mark]*. The last mark is given for a diagram showing an oxygen atom joined to two hydrogen atoms via shared electrons *[1 mark]*. E.g.

nucleus of oxygen atom

shared electrons

nucleus of hydrogen atom

2   Maximum of 6 marks.
In a water molecule, the shared electrons are pulled closer to the oxygen atom than the hydrogen atoms *[1 mark]*. This makes the molecule dipolar *[1 mark]*, which makes water a good solvent for other dipolar molecules *[1 mark]*. Substances can be transported more easily when dissolved in a solvent like water *[1 mark]*. Water is also cohesive due to its polar nature *[1 mark]*. This helps water to flow, which means it can transport substances *[1 mark]*.

Page 7 — Carbohydrates

1   Maximum of 8 marks available.
Glycosidic bonds are formed in condensation reactions *[1 mark]*. A hydrogen atom *[1 mark]* from one monosaccharide combines with a hydroxyl/OH group *[1 mark]* from another monosaccharide. This releases a molecule of water *[1 mark]*. Glycosidic bonds are broken by hydrolysis *[1 mark]*. A molecule of water reacts with the glycosidic bond to split the monosaccharide molecules apart *[1 mark]*. The last two marks are given for a diagram showing a reversible reaction with correct reactants (e.g. two glucose molecules) *[1 mark]* and correct products (e.g. water and maltose) *[1 mark]*. E.g.

α-glucose   α-glucose   condensation / hydrolysis   glycosidic bond   maltose   + H_2O
H_2O is removed

2   Maximum of 10 marks available.
Starch is made of two polysaccharides of alpha-glucose *[1 mark]*. Amylose is a long unbranched chain *[1 mark]* which forms a coiled shape *[1 mark]*. This coiled shape is very compact, making it good for storage *[1 mark]*. Amylose contains 1-4 glycosidic bonds *[1 mark]*. Amylopectin is a long, branched chain *[1 mark]*. Its side branches make it good for storage as the enzymes that break it down can reach the glycosidic bonds easily *[1 mark]*. Amylopectin contains both 1-4 and 1-6 glycosidic bonds *[1 mark]*. Starch is insoluble in water *[1 mark]*. This means it can be stored in cells without causing water to enter by osmosis, which would cause them to swell *[1 mark]*.

Page 9 — Lipids

1   Maximum of 9 marks available.
Triglycerides are made from a single glycerol molecule *[1 mark]* and three molecules of fatty acids *[1 mark]*. They are formed by condensation reactions *[1 mark]*. Ester bonds form between each fatty acid molecule and the glycerol, producing a molecule of water for each fatty acid added *[1 mark]*. Triglycerides are broken up by hydrolysis reactions *[1 mark]*. A molecule of water is added *[1 mark]* to break apart each ester bond *[1 mark]*. The last two marks are given for a diagram showing a reversible reaction with correct reactants (a glycerol molecule with one or more fatty acids) *[1 mark]* and correct products (water and a triglyceride) *[1 mark]*.
E.g.

condensation / hydrolysis   ester bond   + $3H_2O$

2   Maximum of 4 marks available, from any of the 6 points below.
Saturated lipids are mainly found in animal fats *[1 mark]*, whereas unsaturated lipids are mainly found in plants *[1 mark]*. The carbon molecules in the hydrocarbon tails of saturated lipids are joined only by single bonds *[1 mark]*. In unsaturated lipids, there are some double bonds in the hydrocarbon tail *[1 mark]*, which cause a kink in the chain *[1 mark]*. Unsaturated lipids melt at lower temperatures than saturated lipids *[1 mark]*.

Page 11 — Proteins

1   Maximum of 5 marks available.
Two amino acids join together in a condensation reaction *[1 mark]*. A peptide bond *[1 mark]* forms between the carboxyl group *[1 mark]* of one amino acid and the amino group *[1 mark]* of the other amino acid. A molecule of water is released *[1 mark]*.
Make sure you also learn the diagrams for peptide bond formation.

Page 13 — Enzymes

1   Maximum of 2 marks available.
Enzymes are specific because only one substrate will fit into their active site *[1 mark]*. The active site shape of an enzyme is determined by its 3D structure *[1 mark]*.

2   Maximum of 4 marks available.
As the enzyme concentration is increased, the initial rate of reaction will increase *[1 mark]* up to a point *[1 mark]*. This is because the more enzyme molecules there are in a solution, the more likely a substrate molecule is to collide with one of them and form an enzyme-substrate complex *[1 mark]*. But if the amount of substrate is limited, increasing the concentration of enzyme will have no further effect *[1 mark]*.
You can tell by the number of marks for this question that four points are needed. So, make sure you go into enough detail to get all those marks.

Unit 1: Section 2 — The Circulatory System

Page 15 — The Heart and Blood Vessels

1   Maximum of 6 marks available.
The valves only open one way *[1 mark]*. Whether they open or close depends on the relative pressure of the heart chambers *[1 mark]*. If the pressure is greater behind a valve (i.e. there's lots of blood in the chamber behind it) *[1 mark]*, it's forced open, to let the blood travel in the right direction *[1 mark]*. Once the blood's gone through the valve, the pressure is greater in front of the valve *[1 mark]*, which forces it shut, preventing blood from flowing back into the chamber *[1 mark]*.
Here you need to explain how valves function in relation to blood flow, rather than just in relation to relative pressures.

2   Maximum of 4 marks available.
Their walls are muscular *[1 mark]* and contain elastic tissue *[1 mark]*. The inner lining (endothelium) is folded and can expand *[1 mark]*. All these things allow the artery to cope with the high blood pressure produced by the heartbeat *[1 mark]*.

3   Maximum of 4 marks available.
Their walls are only one cell thick *[1 mark]* to allow efficient diffusion of substances (e.g. glucose and oxygen) *[1 mark]*. Capillaries form networks called capillary beds *[1 mark]*, which provide a large surface area for exchange *[1 mark]*.

Page 17 — The Cardiac Cycle and Heart Rate

1   Maximum of 4 marks available.
Pressure increases in the atria during atrial systole and in the ventricles during ventricular systole *[1 mark]*. The pressure in the ventricles also increases as they receive the ejected blood from the atria *[1 mark]*. Pressure decreases in the atria during atrial diastole and in the ventricles during ventricular diastole *[1 mark]*. There's more pressure during contraction in the left ventricle than the right ventricle, because of the thicker muscle walls producing more force *[1 mark]*.
This question doesn't ask you to describe the cardiac cycle — it specifically asks you to describe the pressure changes during diastole and systole. Make sure you mention both atria and ventricles in your answer.

2 a)   Maximum of 1 mark available.
The graph shows a positive correlation/as caffeine concentration increases, heart rate increases *[1 mark]*.
  b)   Maximum of 2 marks available, from any of the 3 points below.
The temperature of the caffeine solutions/Daphnia *[1 mark]*. The amount of light the Daphnia are exposed to *[1 mark]*. The volume of caffeine solution used *[1 mark]*.
  c)   Maximum of 2 marks available, from any of the 3 points below.
Invertebrates are considered to be simpler than vertebrates *[1 mark]*. They're more distantly related to humans than other vertebrates *[1 mark]*. They have less sophisticated nervous systems than vertebrates, so may feel less/no pain *[1 mark]*.

Answers

Unit 1: Section 3 — Lifestyle and Disease

Page 19 — Cardiovascular Disease

1 *Maximum of 5 marks available.*
An atheroma plaque may break through the endothelium (inner lining) of the artery, leaving a rough surface [1 mark]. This damage could cause a blood clot (thrombus) to form over the area [1 mark]. If the blood clot completely blocks a coronary artery, it will restrict blood flow to part of the heart muscle [1 mark], cutting off its oxygen supply [1 mark] and causing a heart attack [1 mark].

2 *Maximum of 3 marks available.*
Their blood clotting mechanism will be impaired/Their blood won't clot as fast as non-sufferer's blood [1 mark] because less prothrombin is available to be converted to thrombin [1 mark]. This means that less fibrinogen will be converted to fibrin [1 mark], which reduces blood clot formation.

Page 21 — Risk Factors for Cardiovascular Disease

1 *Maximum of 11 marks available.*
Carbon monoxide in cigarette smoke combines with haemoglobin [1 mark], which reduces the amount of oxygen transported in the blood [1 mark]. This reduces the amount of oxygen available to body tissues [1 mark]. If the heart muscle/brain doesn't receive enough oxygen it can cause a heart attack/stroke [1 mark]. Nicotine in cigarette smoke makes platelets sticky [1 mark]. This increases the chance of blood clots forming [1 mark], which increases the risk of CVD [1 mark]. Smoking also decreases the amount of antioxidants in the blood [1 mark]. Fewer antioxidants means cell damage in the artery walls is more likely [1 mark], and this can lead to atheroma formation [1 mark], which increases the risk of CVD [1 mark].

2 *Maximum of 6 marks available.*
HDLs are mainly protein [1 mark]. They transport cholesterol from body tissues to the liver [1 mark], to reduce the total blood cholesterol level when it's too high [1 mark]. LDLs are mainly lipid [1 mark]. They transport cholesterol from the liver to the blood [1 mark], to increase the total blood cholesterol level when it's too low [1 mark].
Make sure you don't get HDLs mixed up with LDLs. High density lipoproteins reduce cholesterol when the level is too high. Low density lipoproteins increase cholesterol when the level is too low.

Page 23 — Prevention and Treatment of CVD

1 a) *Maximum of 4 marks available.*
The GP could prescribe antihypertensive drugs to reduce his patient's blood pressure [1 mark]. Lower blood pressure would reduce the risk of damage occurring to the artery walls [1 mark], reducing the risk of atheroma/clot formation and CHD [1 mark]. One disadvantage of taking antihypertensives is they can cause side effects, e.g. palpitations/ abnormal heart rhythms/fainting/headaches/drowsiness/allergic reactions/depression [1 mark].
   b) *Maximum of 2 marks available.*
He could go on a diet [1 mark]. He could exercise more frequently [1 mark].
We know that this patient is obese, so the GP would advise lifestyle changes to reduce his weight.

Page 25 — Interpreting Data on Risk Factors

1 a) *Maximum 1 mark available.*
The number of deaths from ischaemic heart disease/CHD increased as the number of cigarettes smoked per day increased [1 mark].
   b) *Maximum 3 marks available.*
It's a relatively large study, which increases its reliability [1 mark]. But the doctors weren't matched for other factors that could affect the incidence of CHD (e.g. diet, weight, exercise), which decreases its reliability [1 mark]. The doctors may not have told the truth on the questionnaires, which reduces the reliability of the results [1 mark].
When evaluating a study look for things that make the study less reliable (not just the things that make the study more reliable, e.g. a large sample size).

Page 27 — Diet and Energy

1 a) *Maximum 2 marks available*
0.2 mg/cm³ [2 marks].
Incorrect answer but correct working [1 mark]. E.g.

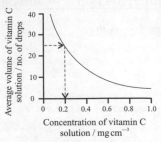

Always show your working — you could get marks for it even if you get the final answer wrong.
   b) *Maximum 3 marks available, from any of the 5 points below.*
Volume of DCPIP [1 mark]. Concentration of DCPIP [1 mark]. Time taken to shake the vitamin C and DCPIP solution [1 mark]. Temperature [1 mark]. Time between each drop of solution being added [1 mark].

2 a) *Maximum 3 marks available*
Energy input – energy output = energy budget,
2000 – 1200 – (2 x 513) – (2 x 328) = –882 [1 mark].
The woman's energy output is greater than her energy input [1 mark], so she will lose weight [1 mark].
   b) *The woman may become (severely) underweight [1 mark].*

Unit 1: Section 4 — Cell Membranes

Page 29 — Cell Membrane Structure

1 a) *Maximum of 5 marks available*
Cut five pieces of beetroot, each the same size [1 mark]. Rinse the pieces of beetroot [1 mark]. Add the pieces of beetroot to solutions of alcohol varying in strength from 0% to 100% [1 mark]. Leave the pieces of beetroot in the solutions for the same amount of time [1 mark]. Use a colorimeter to determine the absorbance of each solution [1 mark].
   b) *The higher the alcohol concentration, the more pigment has leaked out of the beetroot cells [1 mark].*
   c) *Maximum of 2 marks available*
Alcohol dissolves the lipids in the cell membranes [1 mark] so the membranes become more permeable [1 mark].

Page 31 — Transport Across the Cell Membrane

1 *Maximum of 5 marks available.*
Lungs contain many alveoli giving a large surface area [1 mark]. Each alveolus has a good blood supply, maintaining a high concentration gradient [1 mark] by constantly removing O_2 and delivering CO_2 [1 mark]. The alveoli and capillary walls are each only one cell thick, so there is a short diffusion pathway [1 mark]. Concentration gradients are also maintained by breathing in and out, which refreshes the oxygen supply and removes carbon dioxide [1 mark].

2 a) *Maximum of 3 marks available.*
The concentration of water molecules in the sucrose solution was higher than the concentration of water molecules in the potato [1 mark]. Water moves by osmosis from a higher concentration of water molecules to a lower concentration of water molecules [1 mark]. So water moved into the potato, increasing its mass [1 mark].
   b) *Maximum of 1 mark available.*
The concentration of water molecules in the potato and the concentration of water molecules in the sucrose solution were the same [1 mark].
   c) *Maximum of 4 marks available.*
– 0.4 g [1 mark]. The potato has a higher concentration of water molecules than the sucrose solution [1 mark], so the net movement of water is out of the potato [1 mark]. The difference in concentration of water molecules between the solution and the potato is the same as with the 1% solution, so the mass difference should be about the same [1 mark].

Page 33 — Transport Across the Cell Membrane

1 *Maximum of 6 marks available.*
Facilitated diffusion involves channel proteins [1 mark], which transport charged molecules across the membrane [1 mark] down their concentration gradient [1 mark]. It also involves carrier proteins [1 mark], which transport large molecules across the membrane [1 mark] down their concentration gradient [1 mark].

Answers

2   Maximum of 4 marks available.
Endocytosis takes in substances from outside the cell *[1 mark]* via vesicles
formed from the plasma membrane *[1 mark]*.
Exocytosis secretes substances from the cell *[1 mark]* via vesicles made
from the Golgi apparatus *[1 mark]*.
Make sure you don't get these two processes mixed up
— try to remember endo for 'in' and exo for 'out'.

Unit 1: Section 5 — Genetics

Page 35 — Structure of DNA and Replication

1   Maximum of 5 marks available.
Mononucleotides are joined between the phosphate group of one
mononucleotide and the sugar of the next *[1 mark]* by a condensation
reaction *[1 mark]*. The two polynucleotide strands join through hydrogen
bonds *[1 mark]* between the base pairs *[1 mark]*. The final mark is given
for at least one accurate diagram showing at least one of the above points
[1 mark].

As the question asks for a diagram make sure you do at least one, e.g.:

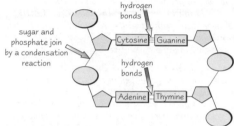

2   Maximum of 7 marks available.
The DNA helix unzips *[1 mark]*. Each strand acts as a template *[1 mark]*.
Individual free DNA mononucleotides join up along the template strand
by complementary base pairing *[1 mark]*. DNA polymerase joins the
individual mononucleotides together *[1 mark]*.
(Students often forget to mention this enzyme in their answers
— make sure you don't forget.)
Hydrogen bonds then form between the bases on each strand *[1 mark]*.
Two identical DNA molecules are produced *[1 mark]*. Each of the new
molecules contains a single strand from the original DNA molecule and a
single new strand *[1 mark]*.

Page 37 — The Genetic Code and Protein Synthesis

1 a) Maximum of 2 marks available. 2 marks for all correct, 1 mark if one
incorrect, no marks if more than 1 incorrect.
GAGUGGGGCACU
  b) Maximum of 2 marks available. 2 marks for all correct, 1 mark if one
incorrect, no marks if more than 1 incorrect.
Leucine, Threonine, Proline (Stop signal).
  c) Maximum of 2 marks available.
At the end of a gene *[1 mark]*, because it has a stop signal *[1 mark]*.

2   Maximum of 10 marks available, from any of the 12 points below.
Transcription happens inside the nucleus and translation happens in the
cytoplasm *[1 mark]*. The hydrogen bonds between the two DNA strands
of a gene break *[1 mark]*, and the DNA molecule uncoils at that point
[1 mark]. One of the strands (antisense strand) is used as a template to
make an mRNA (messenger RNA) copy *[1 mark]* using complementary
base pairing *[1 mark]*. The mRNA moves out of the nucleus and attaches
to a ribosome in the cytoplasm *[1 mark]*. tRNA molecules carry amino
acids to the ribosome *[1 mark]*. tRNA molecules with complementary
bases to the triplets on the mRNA attach themselves to the molecule using
complementary base pairing *[1 mark]*. The amino acids attached to the
tRNA molecules are joined together by peptide bonds *[1 mark]*, forming
a polypeptide chain *[1 mark]*, and the tRNA molecules move away
[1 mark]. This process continues until there's a stop signal on the mRNA
[1 mark].

Unit 1: Section 6 — Genetic Disorders

Page 39 — Genes and Inheritance

1 a) Maximum of 2 marks available.
genotype — Yy *[1 mark]*, phenotype — yellow *[1 mark]*.

b) Maximum of 3 marks available.

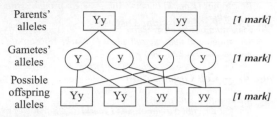

c) Maximum of 1 mark available.
1:1 *[1 mark]*

Page 41 — Inheritance of Genetic Disorders

1 a) Maximum of 2 marks available.
Emma is homozygous for the CF allele *[1 mark]*.
Martha/James is a carrier *[1 mark]*.
  b) Maximum of 3 marks available. 2 marks for the working, 1 for correct
answer. E.g.

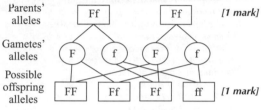

1 in 4/25% *[1 mark]*
  c) Maximum of 8 marks available.
Cystic fibrosis leads to the production of abnormally thick and sticky
mucus *[1 mark]*. The thick mucus can block the tubes connecting the
pancreas to the small intestine *[1 mark]*, preventing digestive enzymes
from reaching the small intestine *[1 mark]*. The mucus can also cause
cysts/growths to form in the pancreas *[1 mark]*, which inhibits the
production of digestive enzymes *[1 mark]*. These both reduce the
sufferer's ability to digest food and so fewer nutrients can be absorbed
[1 mark]. The mucus lining the small intestine is very thick *[1 mark]*,
which inhibits the absorption of nutrients *[1 mark]*.

Page 43 — Genetic Screening and Gene Therapy

1 a) Maximum of 2 marks available.
To see if they're a carrier *[1 mark]*. If they are, this will affect the chance
of any children they have suffering from the disorder *[1 mark]*.
  b) i) Maximum of 1 mark available.
Screening embryos produced by IVF for genetic disorders before
they're implanted into the uterus *[1 mark]*.
    ii) Maximum of 1 mark available, from any of the 2 points below.
It reduces the chance of having a baby with a genetic disorder as
only 'healthy' embryos will be implanted *[1 mark]*. Because it's
performed before implantation, it avoids any issues about abortion
raised by prenatal testing *[1 mark]*.
    iii) Maximum of 2 marks available.
It can be used to find out about other characteristics, leading to
concerns about designer babies *[1 mark]*. Decisions could be made
based on incorrect information (false positives and false negatives)
[1 mark].
  c) Maximum of 2 marks available, 1 mark for method and 1 mark for stating
that the change occurs in muscle cells.
A normal, dominant allele could be added *[1 mark]* to muscle cells
[1 mark].

Unit 2: Section 1 — Cells

Page 46 — Cells and Organelles

1 a) i) Maximum of 1 mark available.
mitochondrion *[1 mark]*
    ii) Maximum of 1 mark available.
Golgi apparatus *[1 mark]*
  b) Maximum of 2 marks available.
Mitochondria are the site of aerobic respiration *[1 mark]*.
The Golgi apparatus processes and packages new lipids and proteins /
makes lysosomes *[1 mark]*.

Answers

2 a) *Maximum of 2 marks available*
       Ribosomes [1 mark] because this is where protein synthesis occurs
       [1 mark].
   b) *Maximum of 3 mark available*
       The rough endoplasmic reticulum [1 mark], ribosomes [1 mark]
       and some vesicles [1 mark].

Page 47 — Cell Organisation

1   *Maximum of 2 marks available.*
    It's best described as an organ [1 mark] as it is made of many tissues
    working together to perform a particular function [1 mark].

Page 49 — The Cell Cycle and Mitosis

1 a) *Maximum of 6 marks available.*
       A = Metaphase [1 mark], because the chromosomes are lined up at the
       middle of the cell [1 mark].
       B = Telophase [1 mark], because there are now two nuclei and the
       cytoplasm is dividing to form two new cells [1 mark].
       C = Anaphase [1 mark], because the centromeres have divided and the
       chromatids are moving to opposite ends of the cell [1 mark].
       If you've learned the diagrams of what happens at each stage of mitosis, this
       should be a breeze. That's why it'd be a total disaster if you lost three marks
       for forgetting to give reasons for your answers. Always read the question
       properly and do exactly what it tells you to do.
   b) *Maximum of 3 marks available:*
       X = Chromatid [1 mark].
       Y = Centromere [1 mark].
       Z = Spindle fibre [1 mark].

2   *Maximum of 8 marks available.*
    Cut a root tip from a growing root [1 mark]. Place it on a watch glass and
    add a few drops of hydrochloric acid to the root tip [1 mark], followed by
    an appropriate stain (e.g. toluidine blue, acetic orcein, Schiff's reagent,
    Feulgen's reagent) [1 mark]. Warm the watch glass [1 mark]. Place the
    root tip on a microscope slide and use a mounted needle to break it open
    and spread the cells out [1 mark]. Add a few more drops of stain and
    place a cover slip over the root tip [1 mark]. Gently squash the cover slip
    down [1 mark]. Warm the slide to intensify the stain [1 mark].

Unit 2: Section 2 — Sexual Reproduction

Page 51 — Production of Gametes

1   *Maximum of 3 marks available.*
    Sperm have flagella/tails, which allow them to swim/move towards the
    egg cell [1 mark]. They contain lots of mitochondria to provide the
    energy needed for swimming/movement [1 mark]. The acrosome in the
    sperm head contains digestive enzymes that break down the egg cell's
    zona pellucida, enabling the sperm to penetrate the egg [1 mark].

2 a) *Maximum of 5 marks available.*
       Before the first division of meiosis, homologous pairs of chromosomes
       come together and pair up [1 mark]. The chromatids twist around each
       other [1 mark]. Bits of the chromatids break off and rejoin onto the other
       chromatid [1 mark]. The chromatids now contain different combinations
       of alleles [1 mark]. This means each of the four daughter cells will contain
       chromatids with different combinations of alleles [1 mark].
   b) *Maximum of 2 marks available.*
       Independent assortment means the chromosome pairs can split up in any
       way [1 mark]. So, the cells produced can contain any combination of
       maternal and paternal chromosomes with different alleles [1 mark].

Page 53 — Fertilisation

1 a) *Maximum of 4 marks available.*
       A = Pollen tube [1 mark].
       B = Embryo sac [1 mark].
       C = Tube nucleus [1 mark].
       D = Micropyle [1 mark].
   b) *Maximum of 2 marks available.*
       The enzymes digest surrounding cells [1 mark], providing a path to the
       ovary [1 mark].

2   *Maximum of 9 marks available.*
    During the acrosome reaction, digestive enzymes are released from the
    acrosome of the sperm [1 mark]. These enzymes digest the zona
    pellucida [1 mark], which allows a sperm to pass through and fuse with
    the cell membrane of the egg cell [1 mark]. This triggers the cortical
    reaction [1 mark] where the contents of the cortical granules are released
    from the egg cell [1 mark]. The chemicals from the cortical granules make
    the zona pellucida thick and impenetrable to other sperm [1 mark], so
    that only one sperm can fertilise the egg cell [1 mark]. The sperm nucleus
    enters the egg cell [1 mark] and fuses with the egg cell nucleus — this is
    fertilisation [1 mark].
    This question asks you to start by describing the acrosome reaction,
    so you won't get any marks for describing anything before this, e.g. the sperm
    swimming towards the egg cell in the oviduct.

Unit 2: Section 3 — Stem Cells

Page 55 — Cell Differentiation

1   *Maximum of 5 marks available.*
    A totipotent stem cell can produce all cell types [1 mark], including all
    specialised cell types [1 mark] and extraembryonic cells [1 mark].
    A pluripotent stem cell can produce all specialised cell types [1 mark]
    but not extraembryonic cells [1 mark].
    Be careful not to get totipotent and pluripotent mixed up.

2   *Maximum of 6 marks available, from any of the 8 points below.*
    All stem cells contain the same genes but not all of them are expressed/
    active [1 mark]. Under the right conditions, some genes are activated and
    others are inactivated [1 mark]. mRNA is only transcribed from the active
    genes [1 mark]. mRNA from the active genes is translated into proteins
    [1 mark]. These proteins modify the cell by changing the cell structure
    [1 mark] and controlling the cell's processes [1 mark]. The changes cause
    the cell to become specialised [1 mark], and they're hard to reverse
    [1 mark].

Page 57 — Stem Cells in Medicine

1 a) *Maximum of 1 mark available, from any of the 3 points below.*
       Stem cells could be used to save lives [1 mark]. Stem cells could
       be used to improve a person's quality of life [1 mark]. Accept a
       description of stem cells being used to cure a specific disease [1 mark].
   b) i) *Maximum of 3 marks available, from any of the 4 points below.*
           Embryos are created in a laboratory using in vitro fertilisation [1 mark].
           Egg cells are fertilised by sperm outside the womb [1 mark]. Once the
           embryos are approximately 4 to 5 days old, stem cells are removed
           from them [1 mark]. The rest of the embryo is destroyed [1 mark].
       ii) *Maximum of 2 marks available.*
           Some people believe that fertilised embryos have a right to life from
           the moment of fertilisation [1 mark]. Some people believe it is
           wrong to destroy (viable) embryos [1 mark].

Unit 2: Section 4 — Variation, Evolution and Classification

Page 59 — Variation

1   *Maximum of 4 marks available.*
    Environmental factors (smoking) affect birth mass [1 mark]. Women who
    smoked showed a mean reduction in the birth mass of their babies of
    377 g [1 mark]. Genetic factors also affect birth mass of babies born to
    women who smoke [1 mark]. The reduction in birth mass was as much as
    1285 g among women who smoked and had certain genotypes [1 mark].

Page 61 — Adaptation and Evolution

1   *Maximum of 3 marks available.*
    Niche is the role of a species within its habitat [1 mark]. It includes the
    organism's interactions with other living organisms [1 mark] and its
    interactions with the non-living environment [1 mark].

Answers

2   Maximum of 8 marks available.
    Behavioural — It can roll into a ball when alarmed [1 mark],
    which increases it chance of escaping attack [1 mark].
    Physiological — It can hibernate over winter [1 mark], which means it's
    more likely to survive the winter months when food is scarce [1 mark].
    For anatomical you can get any two from the list below, to a maximum of 4
    marks — 1 mark for each adaptation and 1 mark for explaining why each
    adaptation increases survival.
    Anatomical — Brown colour [1 mark], camouflages it, so it's harder for
    predators to spot [1 mark]. Spiky fur [1 mark], protects it from predators
    [1 mark]. Long fur [1 mark], provides warmth [1 mark]. Small ears
    [1 mark], help to reduce heat loss [1 mark]. Claws [1 mark], are used to
    catch prey [1 mark].

3   Maximum of 5 marks available.
    Individuals within a population show variation in their phenotypes
    (characteristics) [1 mark]. Predation, disease and competition create a
    struggle for survival [1 mark]. Individuals with better adaptations are
    more likely to survive, reproduce and pass on their advantageous
    adaptations to their offspring [1 mark]. Over time, the number of
    individuals with the adaptations increases [1 mark]. Over generations the
    adaptations become more common in the population [1 mark].

Page 63 — Classification

1 a) Maximum of 2 marks available — two marks for all correct, one mark for
      three, four or five correct.

	Kingdom	Phylum	Class	Order	Family	Genus	Species
Humans	Animalia	Chordata	Mammalia	Primates	Hominidae	Homo	sapiens
Bonobos	Animalia	Chordata	Mammalia	Primates	Hominidae	Pan	paniscus

   You've been given the genus and species name in the introduction when you're
   told the binomial name (Pan paniscus) and because bonobos and humans are in
   the same family, they must be together in all the groups higher than this level.

  b) Maximum of 4 marks available.
      Bonobos must be multicellular [1 mark] with eukaryotic cells [1 mark].
      Their cells must have no cell walls [1 mark]. They must be heterotrophic
      (consume plants and animals) [1 mark].

Unit 2: Section 5 — Resources from Plants

Page 65 — Plant Cell Structure and Plant Stems

1 a) Maximum of 2 marks available.
      X — sclerenchyma fibres [1 mark], Y — xylem vessels [1 mark]
  b) Maximum of 9 marks available.
      The function of xylem vessels is to transport water and mineral ions, and
      provide support [1 mark]. The function of sclerenchyma fibres is to
      provide support [1 mark]. The cells of xylem and sclerenchyma are longer
      than they are wide [1 mark] and they have no cytoplasm [1 mark].
      They are both also made of dead cells, joined end to end [1 mark].
      The xylem have no end walls [1 mark]. The cell walls of both are
      thickened with lignin, which helps to support the plant [1 mark].
      The cell walls of sclerenchyma have more cellulose than xylem vessels
      [1 mark]. Water and mineral ions pass into and out of xylem cells
      through pits in the walls where there's no lignin [1 mark].

Page 67 — Starch, Cellulose and Fibres

1 a) Maximum of 4 marks available.
      The cell wall contains cellulose microfibrils in a net-like arrangement
      [1 mark]. The strength of the microfibrils [1 mark] and their arrangement
      in the cell wall [1 mark] makes plant fibres strong [1 mark].
  b) Maximum of 4 marks available.
      Secondary thickening is the production of another cell wall between the
      normal cell wall and the cell membrane [1 mark]. The secondary cell wall
      is thicker [1 mark] and usually has more lignin than the normal cell wall
      [1 mark]. This also gives plant fibres lots of strength [1 mark].

2 a) Maximum of 8 marks available.
      The students could have attached each of the four fibres to a clamp stand
      at one end [1 mark] and hung weights from the other end [1 mark].
      Weights could then have been added one at a time to each of the fibres,
      until they all broke [1 mark]. They would then have recorded the mass
      taken to break each fibre [1 mark]. They could have done repeat
      experiments for each of the fibres [1 mark]. They should also have
      ensured that all the fibres tested were of the same length [1 mark]. They
      should have kept all other variables constant, like the temperature and
      humidity of the environment [1 mark], and they should have taken safety
      precautions, such as wearing protective goggles/making sure the area

where the weights fall was clear [1 mark].
  b) Maximum of 2 marks available.
      Fibre B would be most suitable [1 mark] because it has the highest tensile
      strength/can hold the most weight without breaking [1 mark].

Page 69 — Sustainability and Plant Minerals

1   Maximum of 6 marks available.
    Take a number of plant seedlings, and plant them in separate pots
    [1 mark]. They should all be the same age and height [1 mark].
    Make up nutrient broths that contain different concentrations of nitrate
    ions [1 mark]. Split the plants into equal sized groups and give each
    group one of the broths you have made up [1 mark]. After several weeks,
    measure the height of the plants, to see how the growth has been affected
    [1 mark]. During the investigation, you need to keep all other variables
    constant, such as the amount of light and water the plants receive
    [1 mark].

Page 71 — Drug Testing and Drugs from Plants

1   Maximum of 5 marks available.
    William Withering made a chance observation — a patient suffering
    from dropsy made a good recovery after being treated with a traditional
    remedy containing foxgloves [1 mark]. Digitalis is found in foxgloves
    [1 mark]. He tested different versions of the remedy containing different
    concentrations of digitalis [1 mark]. He found that too much digitalis
    poisoned his patients, while too little had no effect [1 mark]. Through this
    trial and error method, he discovered the right amount to give to his
    patients [1 mark].

2 a) Maximum of 10 marks available.
      Take an extract from the plant you want to test by drying and grinding the
      plant [1 mark], then soaking it in ethanol [1 mark]. Filter off the liquid bit
      [1 mark]. Evenly spread a sample of bacteria on an agar/nutrient plate
      [1 mark]. Dip a disc of absorbent paper in the plant extract [1 mark].
      Soak a disc in ethanol to act as a control [1 mark]. Place the discs on the
      plate, widely spaced apart [1 mark]. Incubate the plate to allow the
      bacteria to grow [1 mark]. If the plant has antibacterial properties there'll
      be an inhibition zone/clear patch on the lawn of bacteria [1 mark].
      There should be no inhibition zone around the control disc [1 mark].
  b) Maximum of 7 marks available.
      The first phase involves testing the drug on a small group of healthy
      individuals [1 mark]. It's done to identify any side effects, the safe dosage
      and how the body reacts to the drug [1 mark]. The second phase involves
      testing the drug on a large group of patients [1 mark]. It's done to see
      how well the drug works [1 mark]. The third phase involves testing the
      drug on a very large group of patients [1 mark]. It's done to compare the
      effectiveness of the drug with existing drugs [1 mark]. Patients are
      randomly split into two groups, one which receives the new drug, and one
      which receives an existing treatment [1 mark].

Unit 2: Section 6 — Biodiversity

Page 73 — Biodiversity and Endemism

1 a) Maximum of 1 mark available.
      Endemic (endemism) [1 mark].
  b) Maximum of 2 marks available.
      To measure the biodiversity of finches within a single habitat you could
      count the number of different species present in the habitat / you could
      find the species richness / you could count the number of different species
      and the abundance of each species and then used a biodiversity index to
      calculate species diversity [1 mark]. To measure the biodiversity within a
      single finch species you could find the genetic diversity / you could count
      the variety of phenotypes present / you could sequence the DNA of
      individuals and compare them with each other [1 mark].

Page 75 — Conservation of Biodiversity

1   Maximum of 4 marks available.
    It might be difficult to recreate the exact conditions of the lizard's
    environment in captivity, so they may have problems breeding [1 mark].
    Some people think it's cruel to keep animals in captivity, even if it's done
    to prevent them becoming extinct [1 mark]. The reintroduced lizards
    could bring new diseases to the habitat, harming any organisms that are
    already there [1 mark]. Because they were born in captivity, any
    reintroduced lizards may not exhibit all their natural behaviours in the wild
    (e.g. they may have problems finding food or communicating with other
    members of their species) [1 mark].

Index

Index

Index